STANLEY

PETER GUNNING

BLACKWATER PRESS

For Finbarr and Sinéad

© Copyright Peter Gunning
First Published in 1993 by
Blackwater Press,
Airton Road,
Tallaght,
Dublin 24.

Printed at the press of the publisher.

Editor:	Deirdre Whelan
Illustrator/Designer:	Turlough McKevitt
Typesetting:	Professional Mac Services

ISBN: 0 86121 409 9
British library cataloguing in publication data.
A catalogue record of this book is available from the British Library.
Gunning, Peter. Stanley

– CONTENTS –

Chapter 1
The Early Days

Stanley McGregor looked perfectly normal. He was never the tallest of children but at the same time he was no shrimp. He was thin but not in a skinny, bony sort of way. He had a definite shade of blue eyes and his hair was a common sandy brown, combed from left to right with a sharp crease. He walked with a lively skip in his step and, like most boys, always seemed to have both hands dug deeply into his trouser pockets.

To look at Stanley therefore, one might have been of the opinion that he was just another normal young boy. There, unfortunately, one would have been very much mistaken. Our Stanley was not normal. Our Stanley was very, very different. I should know. I'm his father.

It didn't take my wife Ber and I long to discover that Stanley Paul Francis McGregor was different from other children. In fact he was only a few seconds old when he gave us our first shock. As you may know, all newly born babies give a loud cry. This helps their lungs to start working on their own and is the first step in a lifetime of independent breathing.

Stanley, however, had other ideas. He was born holding his breath. With his two eyes shut tightly and both cheeks puffed out he seemed to be refusing to breathe. Doctor Brandon, who delivered him, catching him by the ankles with one hand, turned him upside down and gave him a good hard whack on the rump with the other. Stanley just puffed out his cheeks even more until his whole head looked like an over-ripe tomato.

Turning him up the right way and with nurses panicking and running here there and everywhere Doctor Brandon tried to force Stanley's mouth open. It was then that Stanley did it. He let out a huge ear-piercing shriek of laughter. Doctor Brandon tried to stay calm but I couldn't help but notice his huge hands tremble as he passed the baby to its mother. Ber and I just stared at each other in disbelief. To this day we still don't know which of us had turned the paler shade of white. We did know however that from that

hair-raising moment on, our new bundle of joy was going to be more than a handful!

The next few days were spent in the hospital, with Ber recuperating from the birth and Stanley baffling medical science. Nurses who had worked at St. James' for most of their working lives swore they had never come across a baby like our Stanley. Instead of sucking his thumb like all infants Stanley could be seen regularly lying on the flat of his back with both little fingers stuck in each corner of his mouth as if he were preparing to give a loud wolf whistle!

Sister O'Hara, while doing her rounds one night, noticed something unusual in Stanley's cubicle. She couldn't see him. Stanley had covered himself completely with his blanket. Quietly she entered the cubicle and turned on the light at the side of the cot. She had just rolled back the blanket

when she jumped back with
a heart-stopping fright.
Stanley was lying there with
his left foot stuck firmly in
his mouth. It may only
be a rumour but a
student nurse who hap-
pened to be feeding a baby
in an adjoining cubicle claims
Sr. O'Hara uttered a rather rude word before blessing her-
self and making a hasty exit.

The same student nurse did not escape the attentions of
our Stanley either, however. She was passing his cubicle
later that same night when she spotted Stanley wide awake
and gurgling happily in his cot. Pausing to observe this
pleasant sight she thought Stanley jerked his head slightly.
She entered the cubicle to have a closer look and as she did
the jerking repeated. It actually was more of a twitch than a
jerk and Stanley gave a little contented giggle each time.

It was only when she got right up close to the cot, however, that she understood what Stanley was doing. He was
winking at her! At the tender age of three days Stanley was
winking at women. The young nurse laughed so heartily
she attracted the attention of a rather irritable and imposing
matron who waddled into the cubicle as quickly as her two
flat feet could transport her.

"Nurse! Will you kindly control yourself!" she barked.

"But matron, look! He is winking at me!" replied the young woman who was at this stage barely able to speak through her laughing fit.

"Don't be ridiculous, girl! The child is only three days old! He can't even see you let alone wink at you!"

At this point the matron shoved the nurse out of her way and gazed at Stanley. Stanley stared up from his cot at the wobbly nose and twisted mouth of the matron. Without doubt this was the worst sight he had experienced since entering the world and quite probably he might never see anything more gross before exiting it.

Black hairs with a green tinge hung loosely from each cave-like nostril. Under each eye was a multi-lined deep brown bag. Her wrinkled facial skin contained numerous blackheads and pimples and a huge mountain-shaped wart rose to a sharp peak between her beady eyes. It was little wonder she had earned the title "The Matterhorn". This woman neither received nor deserved a wink! Instead Stanley closed his eyes firmly, gave a loud belch and stuck out his tongue making a very rude rasping sound in the process.

The matron bristled with both horror and humiliation! She stormed out of the cubicle leaving the student nurse in a state of doubled-up convulsion. When she had pulled herself together she peeped into the cot hoping for one last wink from her pint-sized admirer. However Stanley had had quite enough of women and their antics for one night. All that winking had thoroughly exhausted him. He had nodded off with his foot lodged tightly in his mouth!

When Ber had sufficiently recovered from both the birth and the shock of the held-breath incident, it was decided that both she and Stanley could be sent home. Maybe it was just my imagination but I had a funny feeling the hospital staff were glad to see us go. A huge crowd of nurses and doctors flocked at the main doors of the hospital to wave us good-bye. Relief was visible on each of their smiling faces. They stood there waving almost impatiently as I drove slowly through the hospital gates.

Ber sat in the back seat with a seemingly sound asleep Stanley cradled lovingly in her arms. It was a happy moment for us all. As I was just about to turn right onto the main road I heard a wicked snigger from behind. Turning to Ber I asked her what she found so amusing. She informed me she hadn't made a sound. It was Stanley.

He giggled all the way home!

In hindsight the first few weeks of Stanley's life seem hazy in my mind. This is due to the fact that at the time I lived in a state of absolute exhaustion. All new babies make demands on their parents. These demands, such as feeding and changing requirements, can easily tire parents. However, the different and unusual things he got up to made Stanley all the more exhausting.

Before he was born, Ber and I spent many hours reading all the baby books we could find. We wanted to be ready. We wanted to be prepared. None of the books prepared us for Stanley. I never read in any of them, for example, that a baby could punch his mother in the eye. Neither did I learn anywhere that a baby at two weeks old can hold milk in its mouth for over twenty minutes before spitting it between his father's eyes as he attempts to put him to bed. He also continued to wink and stick out his tongue to both the delight and horror of his respective victims.

Of course Stanley did all the other things which normal babies do. He drank a lot. He slept a lot. He wee-ed and pooh-ed so often he must have used about three million disposable nappies. He also caught me every changing time with the same trick.

When I removed his nappy he would point downwards

as if there was something wrong. Then as I would stoop to get a closer look at the source of the trouble he would let fly. A fountain right between the eyes! I'm sure he was the only baby whose parents changed him wearing protective goggles!

Despite these and the other crazy things he continued to do we soon learned how to cope with our zany infant son. Even though exhausted we survived those initial weeks. The foot sucking, milk spitting, laughing and winking all became part of life with Stanley and we accepted it all as normal. In those weeks we formed a very special bond with our new, if somewhat strange, arrival. I might even suggest that the next few weeks went smoothly. However one episode would make such a suggestion untrue. I must not, could not and will not ever forget the christening.

Chapter 2
The Christening

Father McDonagh was a small stout man with a large red nose. It was the town's worst kept secret that the colouring of his nose stemmed from his love of whiskey and other alcoholic beverages. He could be seen regularly wobbling merrily along on his push-bike singing Latin hymns in a deep, if some-what slurred, tenor voice. He was also given to tremendous swings of mood. One day he might greet his parishioners in a bright and bubbly fashion. The next day however, he might not greet them at all but rather walk right past them with his head buried deep in his chest.

He once gave a man two Hail Marys as a penance for using bad language to his wife. When the man returned to confession a month later and admitted the same sin a rather vexed Fr. McDonagh snapped at him viciously saying, "You will hang by the neck until death and may The Lord have mercy on your soul!" The poor man got such a fright he fled from the confessional box and raced all the way home. He threw his arms around his baffled wife for the first time in years and promised her that he would never utter a bad word to her for the rest of his days!

As well as these swings in mood Fr. McDonagh was also very absentminded. He once arrived at a wedding two weeks after the appointed day. The couple were eventually married by the curate and they were back from their honeymoon before Fr. McDonagh turned up to tie the knot!

At a funeral one morning he turned to the coffin and said, "Do you take this woman to be your lawfully wedded wife, to love and to cherish all the days of your life...oh sorry! Wrong page!" The dead man's wife screamed in horror. It was rumoured that she got such a shock that she nearly joined her husband!

Therefore when Father McDonagh arrived at my door, when Stanley was six weeks old, I really didn't know what to expect. In fact it was a very friendly visit with Stanley's christening plans being the main topic of conversation. Ber and I hadn't really thought about the matter very much up until that point. We were both so exhausted from trying to cope with Stanley that spiritual matters were very much pushed to one side.

However, Fr. McDonagh was both a persuasive and forceful man. He was also very sweet toothed! By the time he left our house that night he had consumed a packet of coconut creams, six jam doughnuts plus four mugs of tea with five spoons of sugar in each.

He also left with the christening date pencilled into his diary. It was to be held one week later, Saturday the third of June, at six pm.

We immediately swung into action. 'Operation Baptise Baby' had begun! It actually only took about twenty minutes to complete the plans as all we really had to do was to telephone my brother and Ber's sister and ask them to be godparents. They were both delighted to be asked and were ready and willing to oblige.

Both sets of grandparents were then contacted and were thrilled that we were not abandoning Stanley's soul to eternal damnation! We spent the rest of the evening eating Father McDonagh's leftovers and planning a little party for after the christening. We decided on a buffet with some nice savouries and tarts and a few bottles of champagne. It was a special occasion, after all.

The appointed day arrived and our guests all assembled in our front room an hour before the ceremony was due to begin. My brother Tom, who works as a hotel manager in Kerry, arrived with his wife Sue that morning. Ber's sister Maureen and her husband Phil had arrived from Dublin the night before. It was the first time that any of them had actually seen Stanley and none of them would believe the horror stories we had told them about him.

In fact, even though his behaviour up to now had branded him a little devil, his performance on this occasion was more in keeping with that of an angel. He cooed and laughed and gurgled and chuckled as he was passed from each doting aunt to adoring uncle.

He startled Sue with his winking trick but she was quite flattered when we explained that he did this to every attractive female face!

As I watched this wonderfully well behaved infant in my front room, one hour before his christening, I thought for a while that a miracle was taking place. Maybe now the milk squirting, the hysterical laughing, the wees in the face and all the other inexplicable behaviour patterns would cease. Maybe on this his christening day he would become just another normal little boy. Maybe God was smiling down on me saying, "Okay Buster, you've had it tough up until now, but since you've decided to baptise him I'll use my influence and turn him into a regular little guy!" My imagination was working overtime as I watched my worries disappear. It was a case of wishful thinking, I'm afraid. Stanley was only warming up!

We had never in fact decided to call him Stanley. It isn't a name on my family tree. Neither is it a name associated with any member of Ber's family. To be honest, and this is no offence to any person of that name, it is one which I personally do not like very much. We had decided to call him Paul Francis. Paul is my father's name and Francis, or Frank as he prefers to be called, is the name of Ber's dad. So it was with these names in mind that we set off to St. Martin's to have our baby christened.

Both grandads, along with grannies, were waiting for us at the main doors of the church. They were all so proud as we walked towards them with the guest of honour dressed in a beautiful handcrafted christening robe. He was the first grandchild on either side and each of the grandparents thought that the sun, the moon and the stars radiated their light through him. They had him totally spoilt with presents. At times it seemed as if they were competing for his attention.

At the back of the church that evening he was passed from one to the next as his physical features were discussed in minute detail. They argued politely as to which side of the family he most resembled. He had his Uncle John's eyes, his mother's nose, his grandad's mouth, his Aunt Monica's ears, his Uncle Tom's shaped face and his father's high forehead. I had to take him back from them before they undressed him to discover from which side of the family his bottom came!

Anyway, there we all were at the main entrance of the church waiting for Father McDonagh to formally welcome us as we were told that this was common practice on such an occasion. It's a pity nobody told Father McDonagh. After ten minutes Tom suggested that we move inside the church and he would go to find the priest whom he expected would be in the sacristy. Knowing Father McDonagh's history of absentmindedness, it was felt that this was a very good idea as it might have been Stanley's confirmation day before he'd think of arriving! So Tom headed off to find the priest and we strolled up the centre aisle of the church and sat in the front pews.

As he had predicted, Tom found Father McDonagh, red nosed and very wobbly, putting on his vestments in the sacristy. On hearing that we were waiting, he put his head around the door and said in a slurred voice, "I'll be out soon. Don't start without me!"

How we could have done so still remains a mystery. True to his word however, he emerged moments later and walked unsteadily towards us. He beckoned to us with an unsure finger to join him at the baptismal font.

We formed a neat semi-circle around the font and waited for the service to begin, or more truthfully to end! To my surprise the font was full of water. Usually the font is quite dry and one only sees water when the priest pours some over the baby's head. When I looked more closely I discovered the source of the problem. Clogging up the drain filter was a set of brown rosary beads.

Father McDonagh was always complaining about never being able to find his rosary beads. He often said the rosary at funeral services counting the decades on his fingers. Now I knew why. His beads were busy blocking up a water pipe! He had probably left them there from the last time he had conducted a christening. The font was now almost full to

overflowing, but Father McDonagh didn't
seem to notice.

"Now then," he began, "and
what is the little girl to
be called?"

"It's a boy,
Father!" I cor-
rected in a
polite whis-
per.

"Pardon?"

"I said that
the baby is a
boy!" I repeated in an almost word by word tone.

"A boy? Oh yes of course it is! Yes! Yes! Silly me! I
should have remembered that! Now then, what shall we be
calling him?"

"Paul Francis," Ber informed him.

"Paula Frances! What a lovely name!"

"No, Father! He is a boy and we want to call him Paul
Francis!" I said, a little more loudly this time.

"Ah yes! Paul Francis after the good saints themselves!
Much more appropriate than giving him a silly girl's name!"

Not wishing to confuse him even further by telling him
about the child's grandads, I simply smiled politely and
prayed that he would get on with the ceremony. To my
relief Father McDonagh suddenly blessed himself and

started muttering at great speed what sounded like introductory prayers. His head was bowed solemnly as he rambled along. Then he raised his head and hands for a communal "Amen". At that point I knew there was going to be trouble.

From underneath the christening robe I could see Stanley's feet wriggling outwards. Ber was having difficulty holding him. I realised then that I should have held him but I had never been to a christening before - apart from my own which I obviously don't remember - and I presumed that it was normal practice for the mother to hold the baby. Boy, was I sorry now!

Ber did her best to manoeuvre Stanley back into the cradle position but it was no good. She was fighting a losing battle. It was like trying to wrestle with a greasy dolphin! Stanley was working his way out of the robe and getting nearer and nearer to the water font. All of a sudden there was a mighty splash!

Father McDonagh stared in disbelief as a six week old infant smiled up at him as he floated on his back in his bath of holy water! In the confusion which followed I remember

lifting Stanley with both hands and drying him clumsily with my jacket. There were gasps of disbelief from the grandparents while both Tom and Maureen couldn't contain their laughter.

The priest was visibly shaken. His red flushed cheeks turned white as he struggled to control himself and to continue with the service. I held on to the child myself as Father McDonagh began to race ahead with more prayers. Thankfully there were no more swimming exhibitions from our would-be Olympic back stroke champion! However our guest of honour was not finished yet.

As expected Father McDonagh forgot the intended names. He whispered to me out of the side of his mouth,

"What are the names again?"

Before I had the opportunity to remind him, Stanley began to rock vigorously in my arms, freeing his head from the robe which I had held tightly around him. Once his head was free he began to screech wildly.

"Sta! Ta! Ta!" he repeated over and over again in a high pitched wail. "Sta! Ta! Ta! Sta! Ta! Ta!"

"Does he often do this?" asked the priest.

I didn't get a chance to reply as Stanley's screeching was getting wilder and louder!

"Tan! Tan! Tan! Tan! Tan! Sta! Tan! Sta! Sta! Tan! Tan!"

"What's he screeching?" asked Tom.

"It sounds like he's trying to tell us something!" said Maureen, his bemused godmother.

"Sta! Tan! Tan!"

"Maybe he wants to be called Satan!" joked Tom, but nobody laughed.

"The names?" Father McDonagh roared at me.

"Paul Francis!" I roared back.

"Paul Francis," began Father McDonagh in an effort to get the ceremony over as quickly as possible. However Stanley's response was even more hysterical!

"Sta! Lee! Sta! Lee! Sta! Lee!" His screeching had now reached soprano heights! Nothing was going to shut him up. Father McDonagh's face turned from red to white and then to purple. From a distance he looked like a colour blind set of traffic lights!

"Sta! Lee! Sta! Lee!"

"How old is this baby?" asked the priest as the water jug shook in his hand.

"Six weeks, Father!" I replied but I doubt whether he heard me as Stanley's voice boomed around the church drilling holes in everyone's ear drums.

"Sta! Lee! Sta! Lee! Sta! Sta! Lee! Lee!"

Father McDonagh, desperate to put an end to the screams, quickly poured the jug of water over the baby's head and baptised him.

"Stanley Paul Francis! I baptise you in the name of The Father and of The Son and of the Holy Spirit, Amen!"

Stanley stopped screeching. He gave a loud satisfied chuckle, nestled comfortably into my arms and fell into a deep sleep. Father McDonagh bid us all a hasty goodnight and retreated into the safety of his sacristy, closing the door firmly behind him.

When all the photographs had been taken I went into the sacristy and found him sitting on a hard chair staring into space. Both cheeks of his face were puffed out as if he was out of breath.

"Thanks for everything, Father!" I told him.

"Don't mention it, my son!" he said without looking in my direction.

"If you're not too busy we're holding a little christening party back at the house. Nothing too fancy. Just a few savouries and a glass of wine or two!" I waited for him to accept my invitation.

"Mm... I don't think so. Thank you all the same!" came his refusal, "I have things to do. A sermon to write."

"Of course, Father. But if you change your mind..."

"What?... Oh yes!... Mm... we'll see... Maybe later."

*   *   *   *   *   *   *   *   *

Father McDonagh didn't change his mind. The following morning at mass he amazed the entire congregation with the sermon he claimed he needed to write the night before. He spoke at length about the evils of alcohol and the nightmares it can cause when taken to excess. He followed this over the course of the next few weeks with similar sermons.

Parishioners were also surprised that his red nose gradually became more pink and that his moods were a little more friendly. His tendency to wobble when cycling disappeared and the off key Latin hymns were replaced by a tuneful whistle.

Some months later Father McDonagh left the parish to do missionary work in South America. It was a sudden move which shocked several people in the neighbourhood. They found it difficult to understand why a man of his age would wish to take on such a demanding post. However, as my mother said on the evening of Stanley's baptism, "The Lord moves in mysterious ways!"

Chapter 3
Toddler Troubles

By the time Stanley was three years old his list of achievements read like a catalogue of petty crime. In short he was mad! We used to pray for his bedtime to come, simply to be able to have an incident-free hour or two. Even then we were never sure just how long peace would reign as so often we were disturbed by yet another crash or bang from Stanley's room.

His ability to invent mischief was incredible. One day for example I noticed the washing which I was taking out of the washing machine had a most strange and dreadfully sour smell. I asked Ber about it as I presumed it was she who had loaded the machine in the first place. She hadn't. Stanley had. Furthermore instead of using washing powder and fabric conditioner he had used porridge oatlets and natural yoghurt!

He also went through a phase of either tearing or cutting things up. He was particularly crafty at snipping the elastic in underwear. *My* underwear to be precise! It was most embarrassing at work as I felt my boxer shorts slipping from my waistline every time I stood up. There was a time also when I had no buttons left on any of my shirts. Stanley was convinced that all buttons were edible. He decided to collect thousands of them. When he discovered, much to his frustration, that plastic tastes awful he flushed the whole lot down the toilet!

On another occasion he found a wad of ten pound notes in the top pocket of my suit. He decided to make a one hundred piece jigsaw out of each one. Thankfully I apprehended him just before he was about to start on jigsaw number two. Otherwise we would have been living on bread and water for a month.

Thus we tried to keep scissors, knives or any other dangerous weapons out of Stanley's way. Prevention, we felt, was the safest cure. No amount of prevention however could halt Stanley on his ongoing mission to drive us all crazy before his third birthday. It was as if ideas entered his head and couldn't escape until damage had been caused. One idea was as crazy as the next.

One Saturday morning he tapped me on the shoulder and asked, "Coal dirty daddy?"

"Yes Stanley. Coal is very dirty. Stanley mustn't play in dirty coal!" I informed him, rather pleased with the simplicity of my advice.

Stanley headed out to the back garden to play, muttering to himself, "Stanley no play dirty coal! Stanley no play dirty coal!"

I was really thrilled that my two year old son seemed at last capable of taking in something I had said. Maybe now he was developing common sense. Maybe now he was learning from his father the difference between right and wrong. Would good now triumph over evil in the mind of this highly inventive crazy infant? Pondering these points I relaxed in my favourite armchair happy in the knowledge that my son was at last listening to his daddy. Picking up the newspaper I opened the crossword page and set about solving the puzzle while Stanley amused himself still muttering "Stanley no play dirty coal! Stanley no play dirty coal!"

This peaceful situation lasted a full ten minutes until a ferocious thudding and thumping erupted. Jumping to my feet I immediately went in search of Stanley. I found him in the utility room sitting cross-legged and staring at the window of the washing machine as it spun round and round in full programme. Stanley was attempting to wash a hundred weight of coal! With a deafening buzz the machine tossed its contents around in a black sea of soapy water. A black-faced Stanley clapped his coal-smudged hands together with glee as he roared in approval, "Stanley clean dirty coal! Stanley clean dirty coal!"

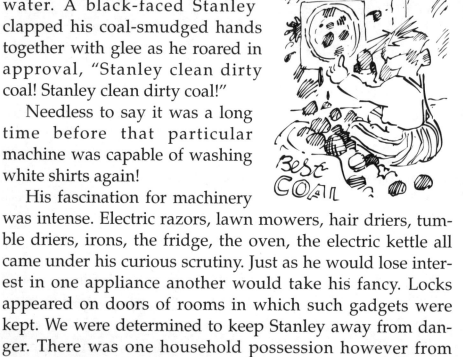

Needless to say it was a long time before that particular machine was capable of washing white shirts again!

His fascination for machinery was intense. Electric razors, lawn mowers, hair driers, tumble driers, irons, the fridge, the oven, the electric kettle all came under his curious scrutiny. Just as he would lose interest in one appliance another would take his fancy. Locks appeared on doors of rooms in which such gadgets were kept. We were determined to keep Stanley away from danger. There was one household possession however from which Stanley could not be separated.

At the time, we had a four year old Alsatian bitch called Zapper. I gave her this name because she reminded me of the remote control for the television. She obeyed commands instantly. She was a beautiful animal with a shiny black and tan coat and dark brown sad eyes. She was unusually slow moving for a creature of her breed.

She walked with a proud gait, moving her head thoughtfully from side to side. By night she would nestle by my feet and snooze, enjoying the heat from the coal fire. She would stay there until exactly ten o'clock when she would rise, stretch out fully, first on front paws then on hind, shake herself and march to the back door. I would then let her out to her kennel which was situated at the back of our garden. Never in four years did Zapper ever disturb either ourselves or any of our neighbours, not even the cranky ones!

However we were worried about having both an Alsatian and a baby in the one house as we had heard some horrific stories about Alsatians attacking children. Even the tamest of dogs can apparently become vicious for no known reason. We knew that Zapper would never hurt any of us but the fact that Stanley was crazy did cause us some concern. Maybe someday Zapper would suddenly think, "I've had enough of this little jerk!" and subsequently dispose of him. However in point of fact it was very much a question of the other way around. Zapper was terrified of Stanley!

The poor creature refused to come out of her kennel if she thought Stanley was playing in the garden. On seeing him she would trot to the end of the garden with Stanley in hot pursuit. He used to do terrible things to her. He would bite her ears, pull her tail, ride her like a donkey, kiss her, hug her, push her, roll her in mud, you name it he did it. Despite this treatment Zapper never retaliated. She would simply wait for the moment and flee to the safety of her kennel. In fact if the Society for the Prevention of Cruelty to Animals knew of the things Stanley did to poor old Zapper I would be behind bars at this moment.

Even though Stanley never intended to show cruelty, Zapper lived in a state of daily terror as she suffered the penance of having a two year old master. It all started innocently enough. Stanley saw Zapper piddling on a flower bed and immediately decided to put a disposable nappy on the unfortunate creature. I remember watching from the kitchen window as Stanley rubbed Sudocrem and patted powder between Zapper's hind legs. A wrestling match then followed between the two as Stanley attempted to secure the sticky fasteners of the nappy and Zapper tried to break free. A humiliated Zapper eventually escaped with a half tied nappy hanging from her rump!

At around the same time as the coal in the washing machine incident Stanley had made up his mind that everything black was dirty. He applied this definition to Zapper. To our horror he found a tin of paint in the garden shed and succeeded in painting Zapper from head to tail! Zapper was the only living creature at the time in "Ultra-Brilliant White Hard Gloss." I remember sprinting down the garden path and snatching both the brush and paint from this pint-sized pet painter. He protested loudly screaming, "Zapper nice and clean! Zapper nice and clean!" as this particular art lesson came to an abrupt end.

The vet confirmed there was no lasting damage done but she warned me that any future "accidents" would not be viewed as lightly. Her advice was to lock up the child and leave the dog roam freely. She also advised that we bathe Zapper almost continuously until the paint would disappear. Several baths and many bottles of white spirits later the paint did indeed fade and Zapper's coat was restored to its original splendour. Believe me though, bathing an Alsatian is no fun. After hours of scrubbing with wire brushes and soapy water all I can say is that I'm lucky I still have both arms!

Zapper was never quite the same after her white-washing experience. She feared Stanley more than ever. She would whimper nervously any time he came within thirty metres of her. However, Stanley never gave up on his quest to drive her as mad as himself. I had to stop him from playing Rodeo on her any time he had seen a western on the telly. Another time he put chilli powder in her dog food.

"Zapper like it hot! Zapper like it hot!" he screamed as the poor beast gasped both for water and oxygen.

All these incidents however were nothing in comparison to the fright I suffered one Saturday evening. Stanley had been put to bed for his usual afternoon nap. Ber was at the hairdresser and I was left to babysit. At about four o'clock I decided that Stanley had slept for long enough and so I went to his bedroom to get him. As I pulled back the bed-clothes my heart stopped beating and a cold sweat burst from my forehead. Lying there sucking Stanley's soother and cuddling his favourite teddy was Zapper.

"Oh my God!" I roared, "You've eaten Stanley! Zapper, how could you?"

I picked up the nearest dangerous object which happened to be an umbrella and was just about to slap Zapper about the head with it when she barked aggressively at me. Dropping the soother from her mouth she jumped from the cot and darted to the backdoor with me close behind her still waving the umbrella. She sniffed at the door furiously indicating that I should open it. On doing so Zapper sprinted down the garden path heading to her kennel. She stopped at the arched entrance and began barking and scratching the earth with her front paws.

"You coward!" I roared, "Trying to escape eh? I'll fix you good and proper, you child muncher!"

I ran after her swinging the umbrella violently. Zapper looked at me with pleading eyes as I came nearer and nearer towards her. She stared at me as if to say, "Stop, you idiot and listen!"

Sensing the dog may have known something I didn't, I stopped and listened. From inside the kennel I could hear a familiar voice – Stanley's voice! I pushed Zapper out of the way and peeped in through the kennel's doorway. In Zapper's straw-lined basket, curled up with a white bone sticking out of each side of his mouth, lay Stanley. I picked him up and he grinned into my face. Taking the bone out of his mouth he drew his face even closer to mine and said, "I Zapper! Mad dog! Wuff wuff, Wuff wuff! I Zapper! Wuff wuff! I bite daddy!"

And he did! He sank his molars right into my nose! As I carried him back up the garden path he continued to laugh and make doggy noises. Meanwhile Zapper stayed behind and watched us re-enter the house. As I closed the backdoor I called out to her, "Come on girl, in you come! Come on!"

But Zapper was not interested. She was sulking. Being accused of eating a toddler was too much for her to handle. She was hurt. She hung her head sadly and lay outside her kennel brooding. The memory of my roaring false accusations and threatening to decapitate her with an umbrella rolled around in her mind. She lay there for hours feeling terribly sorry for herself.

It took Zapper a long time to forgive me. For days she

would retreat to her kennel when she would hear the back-door opening and would only come out again when she was sure I wasn't there. After over a week of this behaviour I decided I'd had enough. I went out to her one night with Stanley. I knew she was in the kennel. I told her I was sorry and that I would never not trust her again. Stanley too offered his words of apology. "I sorry Zapper! I not eat your bone again!" he pledged.

Zapper poked her nose out through the doorway. Stanley screamed with delight and planted a big wet kiss on it. He then shoved a soother into her mouth insisting that she keep it as a present from him.

*   *   *   *   *   *   *   *   *

It wasn't long afterwards that we decided to send Zapper to my cousin Paul, who owns a farm in Kilkenny. Ber and I spent many hours discussing the matter. Neither of us wanted to see her go. She was a huge part of our lives. We had got her as a pup and had taken great delight in training her and watching her develop into the wonderful pet she became.

In fact not only was she a great pet but she was also one of the best friends I ever had. Gentle, obedient, intelligent and affectionate, she meant so much to us all. However to continue to keep both herself and Stanley in one house would have been far too dangerous. Too dangerous that is for Zapper! Therefore, as it wasn't possible to give Stanley away (nobody would have taken him anyway) we decided to contact Paul.

Luckily Paul was delighted to be able to take such a fine animal as Zapper. Paul is a dog lover and has several dogs of different breeds on his farm. Zapper thus would have made loads of new friends. However as we drove to Kilkenny that morning we did so in silence. Stanley sobbed his eyes out in the back seat where he sat for the last time with his beloved Zapper. Despite all the crazy things he used to do to her Stanley adored her. In the rearview mirror of my car I caught sight of Stanley hugging her tightly and Zapper licking the tears from Stanley's cheeks. He kept pleading with us not to give her away, "Don't do it daddy! I love Zapper!" he cried.

I just drove on in silence ignoring his pleas which he repeated over and over again.

We didn't stay very long in Kilkenny as we felt it would be best to just hand over Zapper and go. Paul was waiting at the gates of the avenue leading up to the farmhouse. I explained that we were a bit upset and that we would prefer to drive back home immediately. Being a lover of animals he understood how we felt. Each of us gave Zapper one last hug and kiss. I felt a lump rise in my throat as I rubbed her warm coat for the last time. I then had to drag Stanley away as he held on with all his might to Zapper's neck.

"Come back Zapper! Come back to Stanley!" he roared as tears streamed down his little red face.

Ber wiped her eyes with a tissue as Paul walked back up the avenue. We watched from the gates as they got nearer to the house.

As they rounded the corner at the top of the avenue Paul turned to wave. Zapper too turned to face us with those big brown sad eyes. Waving frantically we shouted more good-byes. Stanley climbed up on to the gate and roared,

"Zapper! I come see you amorrow!"

Zapper opened her mouth wide, turned on her heels and fled!

Chapter 4
Sisters

Although the house seemed a little quieter after Zapper's departure to Kilkenny, it wasn't long before she was replaced. In fact she was doubly replaced as our twin daughters, Córa and Sinéad, were born two months later. I was pleasantly surprised by their smooth arrival into the world. Unlike their big brother, the twins were born with a minimum of fuss and caused absolutely no distress to the hospital staff. There were no breath holding exhibitions, no outbursts of uncontrollable laughter, no winking, footsucking or milk-squirting exploits!

Before their birth I had feared the worst. I suffered a series of nightmares in which I was being attacked by a whole platoon of baby-sized Stanleys, armed with soiled

I suffered a series of nightmares in which I was being attacked by whole platoons of baby-sized Stanleys.

nappies and mouthfuls of undigested milk. In these night-mares Stanley always appeared as the platoon leader and would stare into my face as he ordered his whipper-snapper brigade to unleash their mucky weapons in the direction of my face. Luckily I always woke up just in time with beads of sweat trickling from my brow and flowing down my cheeks.

The nightmares worsened when I discovered that Ber was to give birth to not just one baby but two. Twins! Stanley One was bad enough but the prospect of Stanley Two and Stanley Three boggled my mind! How would I cope? How on earth would my nerves stand up to a treble dose of "Stanleyitis"?

Ber was far more calm about the situation than I was. She is a very optimistic person, choosing to look on the bright side of all things in life. She was therefore delighted when, at her routine visit to the obstetrician, a scan high-lighted the presence of twins in her womb. From the moment she arrived home to tell me I prayed for two girls.

The very idea of Stanley with two *brothers* was enough to send me into a state of panic. Obviously there was no guar-antee that a pair of daughters would be well behaved. With similar genes to those of Stanley, there was a strong chance that they too might view the world from an off the wall position. However my mind was made up. After three years and five months as the father of this zany male specimen, my hopes were firmly fixed. I wanted twin girls.

You can imagine my relief therefore when, in the delivery room of the maternity hospital that night, I became the father of Sinéad and Córa. Stanley was staying with my parents at the time and it was the following morning before I was able to tell him the good news. Stanley was a big brother!

Ber and I had mixed feelings all along as to making Stanley a big brother. We had to bear in mind several negative factors concerning his behaviour to date. Uppermost in our minds was the torture to which he had subjected poor old Zapper. If a fully grown Alsatian bitch lived in total fear of Stanley then what hope would there be for a helpless newborn baby? Then of course, there was his preoccupation with painting things. Would he decide to change the colour of the baby's skin should the mood take him? Would we be the only parents of "Hint of Honey" twins in the neighbourhood? Added to these worries was his love for things electrical. How could any baby be safe in the hands or presence of this wildly imaginative and, at times, near lunatic mini electrician? When we later discovered the impending arrival of two babies these fears were obviously doubled.

Ber eventually succeeded in convincing me that elevating Stanley's status to that of "big brother" might have positive repercussions. New responsibilities might change Stanley for the better. Helping out at changing time by getting creams and powders from the bathroom, or assisting at meal times by spoonfeeding one of his little sisters, might make him see that there is more to life than being a destructive wretch! Maybe now this would be a turning point. At three years and five months Stanley Paul Francis McGregor would discard his lunatic tendencies, abandon his crazy notions and become, finally and not before time, a regular, normal member of the human race. We lived in hope. We must have been nuts.

The first time Stanley saw his twin sisters was when they were two days old. I drove him to the hospital and all the way he talked excitedly about what he was going to say to his mammy and how he was going to give each of his new sisters a really big hug and kiss.

I felt very happy about the whole situation at this stage. We had kept Stanley informed throughout Ber's pregnancy as to what was actually happening. He knew for several months that he was going to have either a baby brother or a baby sister. Indeed, after Ber's scan we told Stanley that he was going to become a brother not only once but twice.

We felt it was only fair to tell him these things. Besides he was very observant and he figured out for himself that Ber's growing tummy was not a result of too much apple pie! We thought that preparing him in advance by telling him the truth was the fairest way of handling the situation. It would have been most insensitive of us to suddenly arrive home with two new babies as if they had been on special offer at the supermarket!

Throughout the pregnancy Stanley had shown great excitement. Sometimes this excitement bordered on impatience. He would yell at Ber to take the babies out of her tummy as he wanted to show them his Duplo garage. She had a bit of a job trying to explain that such an arrangement wasn't as easy as Stanley himself imagined.

On first seeing his new sisters as they lay in their separate cots next to Ber's bed in the hospital ward, Stanley simply stared. His nose twitched. I could see that something was bothering him as his stare switched from Sinéad to Córa and then back again.

"Which one is mine?" he asked.

"They are *both* yours, Stanley!" I replied "Your two beautiful new sisters. Aren't they gorgeous?"

I was trying to defuse the situation before it happened, as I could tell from both his voice and his face that he wasn't at all happy. Stanley was brewing up trouble.

"No, they are not gorgeous!" he snapped.

"Stanley!" I said firmly trying to stay in control, "don't be rude!"

"You said that they were twins!" he yelled at me.

"They are!" I insisted.

"But they are not the same!"

He was right! The twins were not identical. Sinéad was a big plump baby with dark features and a big mop of tatty black hair. Córa, on the other hand, was very tiny with a pinky complexion and no hair on her head at all. I was quite pleased that even though they were twins they had different physical features. Stanley, however, was baffled.

"They gave you the wrong one, Mammy! The baldy one is too small! Swap it for a fat one with hair! I don't like skinny baldy ones!" he said in a really loud voice.

Across the ward from us sat a low sized man who happened to be visiting his wife. He turned slowly on his chair to see who was making all the noise behind him. I cringed when I saw him! Apart from a vague tuft of silver hair behind each ear he was completely bald. He was also very skinny. I immediately tried to silence Stanley.

"Don't be silly, Stanley! Lots of babies are born without hair. It grows within a few months," I whispered.

I hoped this would shut him up. This was very foolish of me. Stanley was on a roll. He wasn't going to be put down that easily. "It mightn't grow, daddy! Look at that skinny little man over there talking to the woman with the beard. *His* hair never grew!"

It was one of those moments when I just wished I could be transported elsewhere, preferably to a Stanley-free planet! The couple across from us scowled as Ber and I timidly smiled at them with a "sure he's only a child" look on each of our faces. They were obviously not amused and resumed their conversation shooting the odd frosty glare in our direction. It was the only occasion in my life when I was sorry that I had hair!

Stanley was totally unaware of the fact that he had insulted anybody. He just continued to stare into the cot. He eyed Córa with a mischievous glint. His nose twitched again. I had to be quick before he caused even more trouble.

"This one is Sinéad and this one is Córa. Do you like the names, Stanley?"

"Yes," he replied without enthusiasm.

Nevertheless I was relieved with his reply and hoped that the lady in the opposite bed might possibly have been named either Córa or Sinéad.

Stanley was obviously not too happy about being the brother of unidentical twins. Córa's lack of both body weight and hair had also caused him some concern. However, as I drove him home from the hospital afterwards, I felt that it had been a good idea to let him see them before they were brought home. I was glad at least that he liked their names.

The following day the twins came home. While Ber was in hospital I had decorated the spare room, converting it into a pink-walled nursery. Stanley, of course, had helped with the painting, although I had to persuade him that pink was a far more suitable colour for a girls' bedroom than his choice of "Nearly Black"!

The first few weeks turned out to be almost trouble free. The twins continued to be the model infants they had been in the hospital and Stanley himself stayed very much out of trouble. Obviously he was a little upset at the intrusion of two new small people into a house where up to now he alone had been the centre of attention. Ber had always believed that this was not a healthy situation for a boy like Stanley. He was so crazy that the more attention he received the more crazy he seemed to become. She believed that sharing the house with two little sisters would make him far less the monster he had been up to now.

Ber was right. Well, she was right for a few weeks at least! Stanley toddled around the house occupying himself with the minimum of bother. He would spend hours in his own room playing cheerfully with toys. He was very gentle with his sisters. He would go to their cots as they slept during the day and rub their cheeks fondly. He also took great delight in singing lullabies to them. This was not, however, a total success. He would sing these lullabies when they were already asleep. They would both wake up screaming! Still, his heart was in the right place.

Cora's lack of body weight and hair continued to trouble Stanley. He was constantly picking her up and plonking her on the bathroom weighing scales. We had to stop him on several occasions from giving her bowls of rice pudding or mashed potato. Ber and I fed the twins using bottles of formula milk. One night, however, Stanley called me to see something on the television. He was watching a nature programme which was all about young animals suckling their mothers. In the course of this programme there was shot of a baby feeding from its mother's breast.

"Why does the baby do that, Dad?" he asked.

"Oh…!" I began, trying to think of a simple explanation, "he does that so as to make him grow big and strong."

Later that same evening Ber and I went into the twins' room to bring them up to the living room for their feed and change. In the corner of the room with Córa cradled to his bare chest sat Stanley. He was trying to breast feed.

"I'm feeding Córa, Mammy! She's too skinny! I'll make her big and strong!" he explained.

Meanwhile Córa screamed in frustration as she tried to suck a cold, flat-chested and totally milkless Stanley.

On another occasion Stanley cut off the head of his teddy bear and removed the stuffing. He flattened out the woolly cloth material and forced it onto the head of Córa as she lay in her cot.

"Mammy!" he roared in obvious delight, "Córa has hair! It grew! It grew!"

Ber rushed into the nursery only to find a bemused Córa lying on the flat of her back with two teddy ears sticking out from either side of her bald little head.

Much to Stanley's delight however, both Córa and Sinéad grew plenty of hair within their first year. Córa also managed to put on weight and by the time her first birthday came, she was nearly as big as Sinéad.

Even though he couldn't read, Stanley would sit between their two cots and hold a big story book aloft. He would then pretend to read them stories, which he made up as he went along, following the pictures for his ideas.

Stanley loved them both. He had become quite used to the fact that they didn't necessarily have to be identical. He was very proud of them and insisted on helping to push the double buggy any time we went out walking. He was kind, gentle and affectionate to them.

Stanley loved to feed them their bottles and when they started eating solid foods he became quite a little expert at spoon-feeding!

Certainly the twins' introduction to our family had a positive effect on Stanley. His overall behaviour improved immensely. However, that is not to suggest for a moment that Stanley's crazy days were over!

Chapter 5
First Day

Stanley started school at the tender age of four years and one month. He became a junior infant at St. Thomas's Primary School. Both Ber and I agreed that Stanley's first day at school couldn't have come soon enough.

There are very few people who fail to remember the moment when they enter a classroom for the very first time. Indeed it is a very special moment, which stays in the memory long after most early memories have disappeared. Starting school marks the end of babyhood and toddler tantrums. It is the turning point marking the beginning of childhood. After spending forty-nine months in the company of Stanley Paul Francis McGregor the baby and toddler, we, his parents, could only welcome the dawn of his childhood days.

School, we felt, could only benefit Stanley. Mixing with

children of his own age in an environment of learning might improve his understanding of "right and wrong". At this stage he only understood "wrong"! Maybe from spending time with these children Stanley would discover how to behave normally. With an emphasis on co-operation and sharing, Stanley might join in and very soon become an ordinary junior member of the human race.

He might, through new skills such as reading, writing and mathematics, direct his energy in new ways, instead of all the time directing it in the line of mass destruction. School might help Stanley at last see that there is more to life than simply driving everybody crazy.

Stanley himself was most enthusiastic about starting school. He couldn't wait. He spent the whole summer counting the days until the first Monday in September. The nearer it got the more excited he became. He tried on his uniform so many times we had to stop him before he had it worn out.

He also learned to tie his own tie knots. He practised on me also. However this came to an abrupt end one evening when he nearly strangled me! Purple faced and spluttering, I made him promise that he would never practise on another human being other than himself ever again. It was a moment when I was glad that Zapper was safe and sound and living in Kilkenny.

Even though we thought it would never arrive, the first of September finally did come. I got up at seven o'clock that

morning. I got ready and went into Stanley's room to call him. When I pulled back the blinds I discovered, to my horror, that Stanley was gone! I checked under the bed and inside his wardrobe, as he had been known to sleep in these places in the past. Not finding him in either, I checked out the twins' room. Córa and Sinéad were both sleeping peacefully and judging from the regular rhythm of their breathing patterns neither had been disturbed by their big brother. Where was he?

I then searched our own room as he often used to sneak in during the night and snuggle down in the laundry basket at the foot of the bed. On those occasions he would pounce out in the morning with a loud screech causing both Ber and me heart failure. However on this particular morning he was not hiding in our bedroom. Ber got up and joined me in the search. Having exhausted the upstairs we tried downstairs. There was still no sign of him.

In the kitchen we found the only shred of evidence. On the kitchen table sat a cereal bowl with a few dried up cornflakes stuck to the bottom. Stanley had breakfasted before disappearing. We extended our search to the garden. Again there was no trace. Just as we were about to panic I heard a strange whistling sound coming from my car. As I approached it I realised that it was not actually a whistle but rather a snore! As I opened the door I found Stanley in the back  seat, fully dressed in his school uniform, fast asleep and snoring like a fog horn.

As I carried him gently from the car to the house, he awoke. In a confused and anxious voice he said,

"Daddy, I've been waiting for ages for you! What kept you?"

"It's only seven fifteen, Stanley," I assured him.

"Is that early or late?" he asked.

Remembering Stanley couldn't tell the time I told him that it was really early.

"What time did you get up?" I asked, not quite sure how he, as a person who had no idea of the clock, would answer.

"When you and mammy went to bed! You always go to bed late. So if it was late I didn't want to be late so I got up!" he said in a matter of fact sort of way which defied logic.

He had me totally confused. I just smiled and told him that in future he was to stay asleep and let me do the worrying about the time. He made me promise I would never in my life allow him to be late for school. I made the promise knowing that it would be an almost impossible one to keep.

Stanley tucked in to his second breakfast of the day. Being up half the night had obviously given him an appetite. He ploughed his way through a plate of sausages, rashers, egg and black pudding and washed it all down with a glass of orange juice. He then packed his lunch box, cleaned his teeth and joined me in the car for the short journey to St. Thomas's.

Even though I had lived in the town for many years, Stanley directed me every inch of the way.

"You turn up here Dad! Down this road Dad! Stop at the red lights Dad! You can go now Dad, they're green! It's not too far now Dad! Turn where that van is turning Dad!"

All of a sudden my four year old son had became both a tour guide and a driving instructor. I realised that my usual early morning radio news programme would never be the same again.

On arrival at St. Thomas's we were met by the sight of

several crying children who were obviously, unlike Stanley, not very pleased about their first day. Some children find the change from home to school very difficult. Some parents, likewise, find it difficult to part with their darling infants. As I walked hand in hand with Stanley through the main doors and up the hallway, neither he nor I had any such misgivings. Stanley couldn't wait to become a schoolboy and I couldn't wait for him to become a schoolboy either. There were no tears. There was no screaming.

We crossed into a wide corridor where the infant classes were situated. Outside one of these classrooms a sniffling mother tried to control her hysterical son.

"I don't want to go in, mammy!" he roared in between convulsive sobs, "I hate it!"

"But you must go, pet," his mother coaxed, "It's a lovely place. You'll meet loads of new friends!"

Stanley glared at this tear filled scene. "I hope that sniffling whingebag of a wimp isn't in my class!" he said angrily.

I pretended I hadn't heard and made my way to Room Three, Miss Treacy's classroom. Miss Treacy was standing in the doorway welcoming each child with a lollipop and a big round badge. On the badge was written the child's name in bold printed letters. "Ah Stanley!" she said cheerfully, "Come on in! Yours is an easy name to remember! I've only one Stanley!"

I felt like telling her that it wouldn't be just his name she would find unforgettable but I resisted. She pushed the door open for us both to see inside. It was indeed a magical sight of both colour and assorted wonders.

The classroom was neatly divided into grouped tables and one side of the room was obviously a play area. In this there was a slide, a foam based trampoline, a rocking horse, a climbing frame, a sand pit, a plastic tunnel and lots of other colourful and exciting items. Painting easels and big mounds of clay were laid out in what was known as the "Craft Corner".

A neat line of child height sinks ran along the wall behind the painting easels. There was also a whole wall of shelves on which sat books of every colour, shape and size. Several children had already spotted where the games and jigsaws were kept and were already noisily, but happily, keeping themselves busy. The walls were decorated with life size Disney cartoon characters, all of whom appeared to be smiling at the beehive of activity in the room.

Stanley stood in frozen silence as he stared at the scene before his eyes. He was transfixed!

"Look at…" he began but he couldn't finish.

"Look at…" he began again but again couldn't finish.

Sensing his joy at the sight of such a wonderland, I decided to finish the sentence for him.

"Yes Stanley! Look at all the super things in the room. The toys, the books, and games, and paints. Isn't it all fantastic?"

But Stanley hadn't heard me. He just continued to stare.

"Look at…" he paused yet again.

"Look at all the children!" he exclaimed as he burst into the classroom, "Hi gang, I'm Stanley! You can all be my friends!"

I was just about to follow him and tell him to calm down when Miss Treacy led me by the arm and firmly, but politely, ushered me out of the room.

"It's best if parents leave!" she said, "Call back and collect Stanley at one o'clock."

"But you don't understand!" I felt I had to explain, "Stanley isn't like other children..."

"Of course he isn't!" she interrupted, obviously not interested in hearing Stanley's life story to date, "Now if you don't mind, Mr. McGregor, I'm very busy! You may collect Stanley at one. Good day!"

She closed the door and there I was alone in the corridor. It was then that I started to panic. I left the school and sat into my car. As I drove out through the gates a feeling of guilt swept over me. What had I done? I had handed over a lunatic son to a poor defenceless teacher! How could she cope? She already had over thirty other infants – several of whom were in tears – with which to contend and now, on top of all that, she had Stanley! This could only be described as an explosive situation. Miss Treacy was alone, unarmed and face to face with Stanley.

My mind began to wander. My imagination went into overdrive. I could picture the scene. Stanley was organising his thirty fellow knee-high monsters in armed rebellion

Stanley was organising his thirty knee-high monsters in armed
rebellion against the solitary figure of Miss Treacey.

against the solitary figure of Miss Treacy. I could hear the crashing of paint pots and smashing of jam jars as they were hurled across the room before breaking into millions of crystal pieces on the tiled surface of the floor. Spilled paint flowed in streams before eventually forming a rainbow-like river. Sinks were overflowing, having been plugged with clay, and water was now cascading like a huge waterfall over their rims.

The classroom was like a scene from a monsoon! Miss Treacy was screaming for help as she hid in a closet behind her desk. However, her screams could not be heard above the roars of the children as they continued their Stanley-led revolt. Missiles of sand and clay soared through the air in grenade-like fashion and bombarded the closet door where they landed with an explosive thud!

The Disney characters no long smiled. Mickey tried to console an hysterical Minnie who was obviously terrified by the scene. Goofy was barking angrily at the children but his bark was cut short when a corned beef sandwich smacked him straight between the eyes! Above all the terrible noise I suddenly heard a car horn.

I was stopped at a set of traffic lights and hadn't noticed them changing to green. The man in the car behind me had noticed and woke me from my daydream with an impatient honk. I drove on to work listening to the radio in an effort to stop my mind from wandering back to the imagined events of Miss Treacy's junior infant classroom.

Though I was busy at work that morning I couldn't concentrate. Piles of uncorrected examination papers littered my desk, yet every time I made an attempt to read through them I failed. My mind wandered and wouldn't stop wandering.

As I drove back to St. Thomas's to collect Stanley shortly before one o'clock, I did so with a certain degree of unease. We were so clear as to the benefits Stanley would get from school, we failed to see that he might be a bad influence on other children. Four year olds who started out as ordinary normal kids might end up as crazy, off the wall lunatics. I waited outside the classroom along with several other parents. I felt guilty. My son was going to change all their children. Maybe they would all blame me if their sweet innocent offspring became uncontrollable little beasts. I tried not to catch their eyes.

Thankfully the door swung open at exactly one o'clock and the children filed out in a neat well behaved line. I could see inside the room and although it wasn't quite as neat and tidy as it had been earlier that morning there was certainly no evidence of any riot. Looking up at the walls I was relieved to see both Mickey and Minnie Mouse offering their welcoming smiles. Goofy too grinned warmly and didn't appear to have been the victim of a well aimed corned beef sandwich!

Stanley was last to appear from the classroom. He emerged with Miss Treacy to whom he was chatting happily. He was covered in paint and both hands were thick with clay. He had obviously found the Craft Corner! Miss Treacy saw me and smiled as she walked in my direction.

"Was he alright?" I asked nervously.

"Oh fine!" she replied, "He's a bit on the hyper side but that's a lot better than being shy, isn't it?"

"Is it?" I asked incredulously.

"He did try to paint the boy next to him green but most of the paint came off eventually. He told me that you once did something like that to your dog!"

She continued to smile at me as she spoke, as if I were some kind of half-wit.

"Me!" I said excitedly.

Stanley gave me a wicked grin! Miss Treacy however continued to speak and returned to the subject of Stanley's first schoolday. "I had to stop him," she said, "from making chocolate cakes out of clay as some of the children ate them and were a little ill as a result. Apart from those little incidents he has been a great little fellow, haven't you, Stanley?"

Stanley nodded proudly. Miss Treacy stood at the doorway of the classroom and was still wearing a broad smile. I stared at her. Was this woman a genius? Was she a magician? Maybe she was some sort of hypnotist and had put Stanley into some kind of trance. She had just spent four and a quarter hours in a room with thirty-two children, and one Stanley, and she was still smiling! She was still standing! How did she do it? As I continued to stare in disbelief I found myself shaking my head slowly.

"Was there something you wanted to tell me about Stanley, Mr. McGregor?" asked Miss Treacy, "I'm sorry if I rushed you away this morning but I really was terribly busy."

"Oh I understand. There's no need to apologise. It was silly of me to try to tell you anything with so much going on all around you," I said.

"So what was it you wanted to tell me about Stanley?" she asked.

"Oh nothing… Stanley is fine really," I lied, "He's as you say, just a bit hyper."

We said goodbye and Stanley and I made our way out to the car. As we sat in, Stanley asked,

"Dad, what does hyper mean?"

"It means you're a nutter!" I replied.

"Oh is that all!" he said calmly as he pulled an apple out from his lunch box and munched it happily.

Stanley continued on his merry way through his first year in St.Thomas's. Miss Treacy soon discovered just how hyper he could be. One day, he organised a Tarzan swinging competition in the P.E. hall. It was free play time on the gymnastics apparatus. The children were busy climbing on the wooden frames or bouncing on trampolines under the watchful eye of Miss Treacy. When a parent came to the door to talk to her Stanley seized his opportunity.

"Come on gang, line up and take turns behind me!" he ordered.

Stanley's plan was to swing from the climbing rope, jump off in mid-flight and land on the trampoline. So successful was his first attempt that he insisted on demonstrating a second time. This time however he became overly confident and swung wildly on the rope.

He bounced not onto the trampoline but off it and crashed into the arms of Miss Treacy, sending her flying out through the doors of the P.E. hall. She was furious and immediately barred Stanley from the P.E. hall for a month.

He was however, hugely popular with the rest of the class even though I did overhear one mother advising her little daughter one morning before school, "Be good now and remember, stay away from that fellow Stanley McGregor!"

When I told Stanley later that I heard this lady telling her daughter to keep out of his way he just huffed.

"That's Helen Barry! She's got no sense of humour. I put some tadpoles in her yoghurt the other day and she didn't even laugh!"

Apart from the little girl who didn't like the idea of live tadpoles swimming around the strawberries in her yoghurt, Stanley made several friends in his first year at St. Thomas's. Every week there seemed to be another birthday party to which he was invited and he was for ever making arrangements to visit other children or else have other children visiting our house.

Of all his early childhood friends, however, one stands out clearly. Stanley will never have another friend like Redser O'Donoghue.

Chapter 6
Best of Friends

Redser O'Donoghue was a beautiful child. His real name was Paddy but with his thick mop of curly ginger hair and two freckle speckled bright red cheeks nobody knew him as anything other than "Redser".

From the first day that they met in Miss Treacy's junior infant class, Stanley and Redser became the closest of friends. They formed an instant bond. Even though they both had several other friends with whom they spent many fun filled hours, Redser and Stanley always seemed to end up together.

Unlike Stanley, Redser was a very quiet shy child. He spoke in a nervous, soft voice and would often blush when asked a question. Stanley appeared to do all the talking while Redser seemed happy to just tag along, apparently doing the lion's share of the listening. They were in fact so different it was difficult to figure out just how exactly they became such great friends. I often watched them as they played and wondered how a gentle quiet child like Redser could possibly be happy in the company of my mischief making and totally crazy son! However, happy together they most certainly were.

Redser and Stanley spent most of their free time in a hilly field known commonly as The Marsh. Even though it was firm underfoot and grassy, it had at one time been bogland before the whole area was reclaimed. To Stanley and Redser The Marsh was par-
adise. They would invent games which usually involved pushing something or some-body downhill!  The Marsh was a wonderland of both excitement and adventure.

They would climb its many and varied trees. Redser's father, Paddy, made the most wonderful timber box cars which they would race over the bumpy ground in Grand Prix Formula One style. In the winter, when The Marsh was covered over with ice and snow, the box cars were replaced by toboggans. In reality these toboggans were milk crates but to Redser and Stanley they were Winter Olympic standard bobsleighs in which they fought for gold and silver medal placings.

Redser's father had cleverly fixed some old tyres onto the branches of mature trees using strong ropes. These sturdy home-made swings provided hours of magical fun. Stanley however, had to be constantly reminded not to jump off in mid-flight, bearing in mind the disastrous results of his Tarzan swinging P.E. games!

Invariably Stanley would arrive home from The Marsh covered in mud and grass from head to toe. As he washed before joining us for dinner (a practice he detested but one upon which we insisted) he would shout stories from the bathroom full of bubbling excitement concerning the day's adventures. Again, as we ate, we did so to the tune of Stanley and his action-packed day at The Marsh. One evening however, I noticed that he wasn't as full of chat as usual. He also appeared to be quite restless. This usually spelt trouble!

Stanley was obviously nervous about something. I noticed that instead of bolting down his dinner as usual, in about five overloaded forkfuls, he merely picked and poked at his food. He seemed totally uninterested in his meal. This was not at all like my son. Something terrible must have happened or maybe it was about to happen. Ber and I ate in silence as we waited. Tired of waiting, I eventually gave in.

"What's the matter, Stanley?" I asked calmly.

"Nothing, Dad," he replied.

"Are you sure?" I continued.

"Positive!" he assured me.

"Really?" I wasn't convinced. I knew my son!

"Yes, Dad! I'm fine!"

Even though he may have thought I was convinced I was far from it. I smelt something wickedly wrong behind his short polite answers. I was soon to discover just how correct was my sense of smell!

"I have a new pet!" Stanley suddenly announced.

I was immediately suspicious. "Have you stolen Gráinne Moroney's rabbit again?" I snapped.

*   *   *   *   *   *   *   *   *

I had tried to blot out the memory of the incident with Gráinne Moroney's rabbit. It was not so easily done. I still recall the details. Gráinne Moroney lived next door to us and both she and her sister Ciara had the most amazing collection of pets. Their back garden was like a mini zoo. They had every type of pet ranging from a tiny white mouse to a python.

That particular evening Gráinne had knocked on our door in floods of tears. Somebody had kidnapped, or rather bunnynapped, her pet rabbit. She clutched a ransom note which had been left in the empty hutch. The note stated that the rabbit would be returned safely in return for a pet lion cub which could be left in a cardboard box under the tallest tree in The Marsh.

Stanley grinned when Gráinne arrived. He listened to her tale of woe with interest.

"That's a coincidence!" he exclaimed, "You lost your bunny rabbit and I found one!"

"You found one?" Gráinne asked.

"Yes! It's in my bedroom!"

We all entered Stanley's bedroom to witness this amazing coincidence. Perched on the bed munching a head of lettuce and surrounded by some half chewed carrots was a large, pink-eyed, white bunny rabbit! Around its neck was a red ribbon tied with a large bow and there was a baseball cap plonked backwards on its head. Stanley had obviously attempted to disguise it.

"That's my Snowball!" roared Gráinne in instant recognition.

"No it's not!" shouted Stanley, "He's my Benny Cool Superbun! Your Snowball never wears a cap!"

None of us fell for this weak explanation. The disguise fooled nobody either! Once the ribbon and cap were removed Benny Cool Superbun became sweet little Snowball once again and was returned with an apology to Gráinne.

*   *   *   *   *   *   *   *   *

This time, however, there seemed to be no rabbit involved.

"I want to feed my new pet. Can you give me some food please, mum?" Stanley asked sweetly.

I wasn't fooled for a moment. "That's no problem, love," said Ber, thinking Stanley had brought home yet another stray dog or hungry cat. He was forever doing this. At times our garden was like the compound at the Cats and Dogs' Home!

"I'll get you a dish of water and a bowl of scraps," Ber promised.

"She won't eat scraps!" Stanley informed her.

"She won't?" Ber was confused.

"I'd say she might enjoy some carrots though!" chirped Stanley.

"You *have* lured Snowball away again! I knew it!" I almost shouted.

Stanley looked at me with scorn.

"I don't even like rabbits any more. I've gone off them. Their hutches pong too much!" Stanley claimed.

"It better not be another cat!" I told him, "You know Córa hates cats ever since you put kittens in her cot and told her they were tiger cubs!"

"Henrietta is not a cat!"

"Who the hell is Henrietta?" I asked totally baffled.

"My new pet!"

"Henrietta a hedgehog?" I was hoping for a miracle.

"Henry ate a hedgehog?" Ber was obviously in a deeper state of bafflement than myself.

"Henrietta a guinea pig? Henrietta a budgie?" I continued to guess, praying for that miracle to be answered.

"Henrietta..." Stanley paused.

"Go on! Tell us!"

"Henrietta a ...horse!"

I jumped from the table and roared at the top of my voice, "How in the name of God could you find a stray horse?"

I ran outside to the front garden and there tied to a pillar was a huge chestnut-coloured mare! I stood at the door. I couldn't move. My mouth attempted to mutter something but my whole body suffered some kind of lockjaw. I just stared in frozen horror at this beast who was munching her way through my flower beds. Stanley stood at my side and was smiling proudly at his captured prize.

"Redser and me found her!" he explained. I was going to remind him to say "I" and not "me" but this was no time for a grammar lesson.

"There are five more of them but I thought I'd take Henrietta for now and maybe bring the others home later!" he continued, as if it was perfectly normal to arrive home with a fully grown horse.

I was still frozen. However, I could feel a sudden surge of uncontrollable anger mixed with frustration rising from my ankles and working its way up through my whole body. I was beginning to hyperventilate. The upper half of my body began to vibrate violently. I became a human volcano. Suddenly in one mighty deafening roar I erupted!

"Get it out of here!"

The words rocketed from my lips. Unfortunately I managed to get rid of the horse myself. The animal got such a fright when I roared that she started bucking up and down on her hind legs and neighing hysterically. Suddenly she broke free from the loosely tied rope.

However, instead of galloping back in the direction from which she came, she turned and bolted in the direction of Stanley and me who were still standing in the doorway. We dived for cover into the hedging as Henrietta crashed through the front door and continued her run through the hallway. On her way she scattered tables, chairs and the telephone table complete with telephone. Thankfully the back door was open at the time and she went straight through into the back garden. Stanley and I gave chase but it was no use. This horse was used to running.

Not content to wait for us in the back garden, she began to leap over the walls of our neighbours' gardens. She crashed through Mr. O'Brien's garden shed and became entangled in the washing hanging from Mooney's clothesline. Breaking free, Henrietta continued her gallop with a line of drying shirts and assorted underwear flowing from her neck.

By now all the neighbours were out. There was an equally amazed look on each of their faces. Well, it's not every day that a horse bolts through your back garden! Henrietta eventually came to a halt in a field at the far end of the estate. There she began munching wild flowers and weeds, having shaken off the Mooneys' washing from her mane.

It was only minutes after Henrietta's hedge hopping exploits that Paddy O'Donoghue called in his van complete with a horse box. Redser had told him how both he and Stanley had been able to mount the horse using milk crates and a rope. They had spent the afternoon playing cowboys in The Marsh! The horses belonged to relations of Paddy who had called to visit before heading to Ballinasloe for the annual horse fair.

The O'Donoghues belonged to the travelling community and lived most of the year in a halting site alongside The Marsh. Paddy had allowed the horses out into The Marsh thinking it to be a safe place for them to exercise as it is fenced in on all sides. When he heard that Stanley had ridden Henrietta home he immediately drove straight over.

Paddy had Henrietta inside that horse box less than five minutes after calling. Stanley and I, together with the neighbours, watched as he expertly coaxed the frightened horse with some sugar. Once he had won the animal's confidence, he patted her fondly and than calmly bridled her and led her to the horse box. When he bolted the door of the horse box there was a huge round of applause from all of us. Paddy blushed. He wasn't used to performing in front of an audience. To him handling a horse was as natural as walking. Shyly, he sat into his van and drove away.

Thankfully nobody was injured by the galloping Henrietta. The damage to property, apart from Mooneys' clothesline and Mr. O'Brien's garden shed was minimal. Mrs. Mooney was quite happy to accept my offer to re-erect the clothesline and to rewash the shirts and underwear. Mr. O'Brien, who is a grumpy man at the best of times, told me that if I didn't fix his shed properly I would have to buy him a new one. Luckily I was able to repair it to his satisfaction and was spared this expense. This was just as well as my new front door cost a fortune!

Redser and Stanley continued to be the best of friends. Together they spent many happy hours whether it was in The Marsh or in each other's homes. Every summer however, the two friends were apart.

The O'Donoghues left the halting site at the beginning of the school summer holidays and did not return until the end of August. Although very content to stay at the halting site for most of the year they longed for these months when they would tow their mobile home around the country. Paddy was a gifted carpenter. He worked for local builders when work was available but his greatest love was for handcarving. He made the most wonderful wooden toys and ornaments. These he sold at different craft centres all around Ireland during their summer travels.

Stanley would spend the holidays counting the days for Redser's return. Although he had other friends to play with there was no-one quite like Redser. His summers were long and lonely as he ticked away the days one by one on his calendar. On his return, Redser would suddenly appear on our doorstep much to the delight of Stanley who would hug his friend as if he was some long lost but now returned brother!

Just what made them such great friends I'll never know. Redser's mother, Mary, often told me that Stanley helped Redser greatly. As a result of their friendship he had become less shy and far more confident. Stanley too gained by learning more about the travelling community, which he would never have done without his friendship with Redser.

It was therefore a cause of much sorrow when Redser left town. One morning at about seven o'clock the doorbell rang. Stanley ran down the stairs to answer the door. As he did so he caught sight of the O'Donoghue van pulling slowly away. Redser peered out through the window and waved at his best friend. Redser's tear stained red cheeks were flushed with sadness as the van crawled slowly out of

the estate. Paddy had told me some weeks before this that he was thinking of moving on. The building trade hadn't been too busy and he had been without regular work for some time. A brother of his was a contractor in Dublin and had promised him a job. He didn't relish the thought of uprooting the family but felt that he was left with little choice. In the end however, they left suddenly. There were no goodbyes.

Stanley couldn't believe his eyes as he watched his closest friend disappear into the early morning mist. Tears ran down his cheeks as he tried to explain to me what he had just seen. I tried to explain to him that this was the way travelling people preferred to live but it was no use. He sobbed bitterly. He loved Redser and no amount of consoling would placate him in this his moment of loss.

There was one thing which did cheer him up that morning, however. Stanley had been so shocked at the sight of the Donoghues driving away that he never thought of looking at the doorstep. On it was placed the most magnificent box-car which Paddy had made as a parting gift from Redser to Stanley. Its doors were of beautifully varnished timber and its frame was made of wrought iron painted black. It had a cushioned driver's seat and a real steering wheel. Its wheels were thick and rubber clad and the pedal powered car boasted strong brakes and an exceptionally loud hooter! On each door were engraved the initials "S.M."

"Well, Stanley," I said when I saw the initials for the first time as Stanley sat in for a test drive, "Paddy even put your initials on the doors. 'S.M.' Stanley McGregor!"

"Don't be daft!" retorted Stanley, "'S.M.' stands for 'Super Motorist'!" And he sped off. As I watched him, I read the card which Paddy had left on the seat of the car. It read:

Dear Stanley,

Thank you for being such a good friend to Redser. He will never forget you. None of us will. Hope you like the car. Don't drive too fast!

Love,

Paddy, Mary and Redser.

As I glanced up from the card I saw Stanley speeding full throttle downhill, passing out a milk float and some startled early morning cyclists. "Don't drive too fast!" I should be so lucky!

Chapter 7
A sporting life

At the age of eight Stanley decided that he was going to become a champion sportsman. The only difficulty with this decision was trying to find a sport in which Stanley could actually compete, let alone become its greatest exponent.

St. Thomas's had several sports teams and each class was given the opportunity to experience each sport. Should any particular sport appeal to a child then he or she was encouraged to either join a club or wait until he or she was old enough to represent the school. In the meantime a whole series of mini-leagues was organised. These involved interclass games and were part of the school's physical education policy.

The leagues started when the children were roughly seven or eight years old and in second class. The games were varied. One week there might be a soccer blitz, the next a Gaelic Football league. There were also rounders, hurling, tennis, rugby, basketball and cricket.

Every time a new league was about to begin Stanley would announce that he was again about to become a champion. By the time the league would have ended he would have proved to all that he certainly made an impact! The first time he played basketball for example proved that, although he was enthusiastic, the sport wasn't quite ready for Stanley! Or rather the sport wasn't quite ready for Stanley's interpretation of the rules.

Stanley's team, "The Wildcats", had progressed to the semi-finals and were to play a team from another class, "The Beavers". In earlier rounds Stanley hadn't been given much time to show his skills, as he had been left on the reserve bench for most of the time. By the time he was introduced to any action, his team were winning by so much they didn't think it necessary to pass the ball to Stanley. They continued to score themselves and Stanley succeeded in finishing each game without ever touching the ball.

In the semi-finals however two of Stanley's team-mates were absent due to illness and Stanley found himself, at last, included in the starting line-up. He was playing in a defensive role under the net. His teacher Mr. Donovan was acting as coach and he told Stanley before the game to simply stop the opposition from shooting. Little did he know just how literally he was to be taken!

The game was only ten seconds old when the opposing team, "The Beavers" were in an attacking position. The ball was smartly passed to a tall lean boy who only had to bypass Stanley to shoot for a basket and put his team into a two point lead. Stanley remembered Mr. Donovan's pre-match words of advice, "Simply stop the opposition from shooting!"

As he turned away from him and prepared to aim the

ball at the basket Stanley lunged his whole body at the boy's stomach. Flattened, winded, badly bruised and breathless, the boy was carried to the side of the court and a reserve was called on to replace him. The referee then warned Stanley who protested that he was only doing as he was told!

One minute later Stanley was in the wars again. The ball was bounce-passed around him and a Beaver player found himself under the net with a clear shooting opportunity. Stanley had to stop him! This time he felt it would be unwise to throw himself at the player. He didn't wish to make the same mistake twice. Instead he chose another one.

This was a less obvious mistake, although equally effective. As the boy rose to shoot, Stanley stuck his foot between his legs and tripped him up. The unfortunate player fell flat on his face as the ball trickled harmlessly out of the court. Stanley begged forgiveness from the referee, claiming that he was never told tripping wasn't in the official rule book. He was given a stern telling off before he was allowed to continue.

For the rest of the game Stanley behaved himself. Mr. Donovan moved him into an offensive position and apart from two completely off target shots and three misguided passes, Stanley was certainly not a major part of the action. However, his team-mates were playing very well and were on level terms with just one minute remaining. If they could just score the next basket then they would win.

It was during this minute however when disaster struck. Correction. Stanley struck! He had wandered into the middle of the court and suddenly he found himself holding the ball. He looked up at the basket and wondered should he shoot. Deciding he was too far out to try a shot and being unable to either dribble or make a straight pass, he hit upon a new, yet totally illegal, tactic. He decided to attempt a drop kick!

He booted the ball as hard as he could in the direction of the basket. The other players stood and stared as the ball whistled through the air. It bounced violently against the rim of the ring and rebounded at great speed. It was the referee who felt the full impact of this rebound. The ball struck him on the head sending his glasses flying and leaving him lying on the ground badly dazed and trying to figure out just what exactly had happened. Stanley had knocked out the referee!

When the poor man eventually got back on his feet he decided to continue with the game as there was less than a minute remaining. The game ended all square at twenty points each. In the end however, Stanley's Wildcats were beaten on a "free-shot shoot out". There's no prize for guessing who missed the vital shot for The Wildcats. This time at least, he did actually throw the ball!

Other sports proved equally and sometimes even more disastrous. Even with all the children wearing protective headgear, face visors and shin pads, Stanley found a way of making hurling impossible. Nobody would play either with or against him. He swung the hurley so wildly around his head he looked like a helicopter in flight!

In attempting to hit the ball on the ground his aim was so poor that the hurley usually ended up implanted some-where between the head and toes of another player, not necessarily on the opposing team. Sods of turf would fly in every direction as he tried in vain to make contact between the hurley and the sliotar. After each game or practice session the pitch would be so full of divots and burrows it resembled the crater-dotted surface of the moon. No amount of coaching would work. Stanley was uncoachable.

He was too wild. A hurling "no go area". In short, Stanley was a failed hurler.

Stanley didn't look at it that way, however. He thought he was brilliant! He felt that neither his hurling coach nor his fellow hurlers appreciated his genius. Nobody had the ability to recognise the new style he had introduced to the game of hurling. He was born too soon. He was ahead of his time.

Stanley found himself sitting on the sideline while the hurling league was in progress. Banned from taking part, he still refused to accept rejection. He pleaded for the opportunity to display his special talents. These pleas were not listened to by his hurling coach, Mr. Keane. On one occasion he argued with Mr. Keane.

"Hurling is a game for men!" he claimed, in defence of his own ferociously violent technique, which had resulted in his being barred from the league.

"Maybe, Stanley... but not cavemen!" came the curt reply.

Despite such lack of understanding Stanley did not give up in his quest. He would find his niche in another sport, or maybe in several other sports. Stanley the multi-talented! Stanley the mega sports star supreme! Stanley the champion of champions! Stanley the great!

Finding greatness was not as easy a task as it seemed, however. Each time an opportunity arose for Stanley to demonstrate his champion-like qualities, he either seemed

to miss it or else to flunk it splendidly. In athletics for example, Stanley decided that he was going to become a champion cross country runner. I figured taking up running was a good idea. Stanley had two legs. He could run fairly swiftly. Maybe here he might find success. However, in his first race over a simple two kilometre course, he disappeared.

The race had started well for Stanley and after the initial lap around the football field he found himself well up with the pack and lying in about fifth position. The next stage of the course took the runners on an eight hundred metre trek through a woodland area. One by one the runners re-emerged from the woods and made their way in Indian file through some muddy fields to the finishing line.

There was however no sign of Stanley. Ber, Sinéad, Córa and I waited patiently for him to reappear from the woods but he never did so. The twins were very disappointed as they felt sure that Stanley would cross the line first. Stanley had made them members of his fan club. They were the club's only members.

When what seemed to be the last of the runners trudged out of the woods and made his way towards the muddy fields, I decided to go and see whether calamity had once again befallen my son. Maybe he had fallen or got his foot stuck in a badger trap. Maybe he had slipped into the river and was now frantically trying to keep himself afloat as the rapids carried him downstream.

My fears were ill-founded. I had only walked a short distance when I found him. Stanley was sitting on the river bank nursing an injured squirrel. I felt very proud of him when I saw him there, gently rubbing the frightened creature's silky furred back. He had had an opportunity to prove to us all that he could be a good, if not a champion runner. Instead he had decided to look after a sick animal. I put my arm around his shoulder and gave him a big fatherly "that's my boy" hug.

"Where did you find him?" I asked, anxious to discover from where the squirrel came.

"I stood on his tail as I was running through," he

explained, "I felt guilty when I heard him yelp so I followed him over here. He's lovely isn't he, Dad?"

"He sure is, Stanley," I replied, "Is he okay?"

"I think so, although his heart is beating very fast," explained Stanley who was enjoying the role of the "would be vet".

"But Dad?" he continued.

"Yes son," I said.

"If he dies… can I stuff him?"

I didn't bother answering. I just grabbed the furry creature and set him off into the woods. He scampered furiously, weaving his way in and out of the tall pine trees in an effort to rediscover his bearings. Within seconds he was out of sight. Little did that squirrel know what a lucky escape he had just had!

My fears for Stanley's safety that day led me to believe that it was time to teach him how to swim. Being a strong swimmer myself with a lifeguard's certificate, I felt more than confident in undertaking the job. Up until now Stanley had always made an excuse anytime I suggested going to the pool. He would complain that he felt a cold coming on, or that the chlorine in the water would make his eyes sting, or that he heard a boy at school say that the pool was infested with rats. After his list of excuses had run dry and he began to repeat the same one twice I discovered the root of the problem. Stanley was terrified of the water.

On his first day at the swimming pool Stanley took twenty minutes to get undressed and then another ten to put on his trunks. When he finally emerged from the changing room he walked nervously to the shallow end where he sat at the poolside dipping his toes into the water. I asked him several times to climb down the ladder and walk around in the water.

"I'm too cold!" he claimed as his teeth chattered.

"Come on in!" I coaxed, "You'll get warmed up in no time."

Stanley pretended he didn't hear me. He did this quite a lot, especially when he didn't want to do something. In the end I swam under his feet and pulled him in by the ankles. Stanley kicked and threw his arms about violently, thrashing the water with both his fists and feet.

"Help me! I'm drowning!" he roared, "This man is a lunatic! He's crazy! He's a murderer! He's trying to drown me! Help! Help!"

Stanley was raving. His screeches attracted the attention of the lifeguard who rose from his poolside chair to see from where all the commotion was coming. He smiled as he resumed his seat when he realised Stanley was in no danger. I was holding him firmly, supporting both his head and his bottom. He was completely out of the water, apart from his still thrashing and kicking limbs! "You madman! Let me go!" he continued to roar, "You'll rot in jail for this! You childkiller!"

"Calm down, Stanley! You're not even in the water yet!" I informed him.

Realising that he had been mistaken and that he had caused a scene Stanley began to relax a little. I gently lowered him onto his back. Despite a minor protest when he told me it was "bloody freezing!", he began to relax even more. Still supporting his back and head I walked around the pool with him giving him the sensation of floating. The same day I was able to take away one hand and he floated happily while I held him up with the other. He then decided that he felt safe enough to walk around and we finished off with some splashing exercises whereby Stanley held on to the chrome bar, which ran along the inside of the pool, and kicked with both legs.

After another few lessons Stanley's confidence grew and as it did his progress developed accordingly. Very soon he was swimming using inflatable arm-bands. The arm-band swimming phase lasted a very short time as Stanley was determined to swim unaided. One afternoon, only three weeks after calling me a murderer, Stanley discarded his arm-bands and doggy paddled around in the shallow end of the pool.

From that day on his stroke and style developed steadily. I was thrilled with his progress. He went from width swimming to length swimming and was able to use front crawl, breast stroke and back stroke. In a relatively short period of time Stanley had learned how to swim. This to my mind, was a wonderful achievement. Stanley, however, was not impressed.

"I'm still not a champion, Dad!" he complained.

This was true. Although he had progressed very well, he swam slowly and was never going to become an Olympic contender in water sports. Swimming, according to Stanley, was for fun and relaxation, but he still wanted to experience the glory of winning! It was then that Stanley came up with the suggestion that he try his hand, or rather hands, at boxing.

I had heard many people claim that boxing is a savage sport and should be banned. My mother hates it and screams in disgust anytime she sees it on the telly. However, I love it.

As a boy I was a member of our local club, The Red Gloves. It was a great club and ran an excellent training programme for fighters. I gave up boxing however when I realised that you have to able to fight to win. After fifteen defeats out of fifteen bouts I hung up my gloves at the tender age of twelve, much to the delight of my mother. However, maybe Stanley might cope better in the ring than his old man!

Certainly both the excitement and enthusiasm which he displayed at training made Stanley a likely candidate to succeed in the ring. All the boxers at Red Gloves are carefully graded on the basis of age, weight and ability. Stanley trained as an Under Nine, Under Forty Kilos, beginner.

Training was organised with clockwork precision. There were ten activities ranging from skipping to punch-bag pounding to eventual sparring. Sparring involved a three minute fight. Both boxers wore protective headgear and stomach pads, and rules were strictly applied by the referee. During sparring, skills such as swerving and connecting were put into practice and gradually the young boxers were prepared for their first competitive bout.

Stanley's preparations were done under the eagle eye of John Malone. John was a former national flyweight champion and could have made it as a professional. However, he retired from the ring at an early age preferring to coach youngsters instead. Stanley progressed well under John who in turn was delighted with Stanley's enthusiasm for the sport. It was with great pride therefore that Stanley announced one evening after training that he had been picked to box for Red Gloves.

Stanley's fight was one of several on the bill that night as Red Gloves were challenging their near rivals, Broadbank. I sat alone watching the first few bouts. Ber had refused to come along and was quite annoyed with me for encouraging Stanley to take part in, as she called it, a bloodsport. She also refused to allow me to bring the twins. The bouts were all pretty even, with most going the distance and decided on points. I had been a little bit nervous all day. I was worried about Stanley and I just hoped that he would be able to cope.

When I saw his opponent enter the ring that evening the nervousness I had been experiencing during the day turned to sheer terror. Stanley couldn't possibly outbox such a ferocious looking monster! Although he was in the same weight division as Stanley, this guy looked about ten times bigger with muscles bursting out of his body in all directions. He

was like a miniature "Mr Universe"! He had a wicked, almost evil, stare in his eye. As he danced about the ring punching the air before the fight, he seemed to be looking directly at me. I felt he was giving me a message. Something like, "I'm going to kill your son!"

I stared at Stanley who was standing meekly in the opposite corner to this animal. I wanted to jump into the ring and take him home with me. He stood there in his brand new boxing gear. He was wearing huge boots with laces that ran from toe to knee. He had shiny baggy black shorts and a Red Gloves singlet. His helmet swamped his head. It was more like a motor bike helmet than one designed to protect a boxer. His gloves looked monstrously huge on his bony arms and hung awkwardly by his side.

I doubted if Stanley had the strength to raise his arm above his shoulder, let alone box with this Samson. John Malone popped a gum shield into Stanley's mouth to complete the boxer appearance. I was still tempted to jump in and stop the fight. It was too late. The bell had sounded. Seconds out! Round One! Stanley the boxer had arrived.

For the first minutes of the fight Stanley behaved more like a ballet dancer than a future Mohammed Ali. He pranced around the ring swerving and twisting on his tiptoes as he avoided the vicious swipes of his far more aggressive opponent. In my mind I could hear the sound of the Nutcracker Suite as Stanley continued his ballet dance and his ring partner shuffled heavily from foot to foot in an apparent war dance. Indeed, bearing in mind that which was about to happen, The Nutcracker was a most appropriate title!

It took just one connecting punch to put an end to Stanley's hopes of becoming an all time boxing great. However, he certainly went out in style! He survived one minute and fifteen seconds of deadly swipes and killer blows by his simply ducking and my frantic praying. However, his luck was not to last. A savage right hook to the nose sent him crashing through the ropes where he landed on the laps of the ringside judges. There he lay as the referee counted to ten, before raising the arm of the other boy signifying his victory. Meanwhile his victim gradually began to wake up as he was passed from the laps of the judges into my awaiting arms.

I carried him to the changing room where I remember tapping his face in an effort to revive him. When he eventually came to, he stared into my face and said,

"Okay Dad! I'm ready! Let's go for it!"

Later that evening in the safety of the kitchen at home Stanley announced his decision to retire from the ring. His throbbing nose and swollen lip had helped him to come to this decision. Ber was thrilled and immediately telephoned my mother to tell her the good news. I must admit to feeling relieved myself. My blood pressure would not have been up to another exhibition from my tip-toeing boxer son. It was also nice to have my wife speaking to me again!

Having proved a disaster at most sports Stanley eventually decided not to become a champion. He came to realise that sport is not all about being the best. It's about enjoyment. It's about having a go. It's about taking part. Above all else he discovered that sport is about having fun.

He continued to try his best but he no longer became upset if his best was not good enough. He enjoyed the odd game of football and even taught himself how to use a hurley... properly!

Swimming became a regular form of exercise and he also loved to cycle. Best of all however, he would enjoy and grow to love the sport of fishing. This was due in no small way to my own father or, as Stanley called him, Gramps.

Chapter 8
Gramps

Stanley's ninth birthday was a completely different affair from that of his eighth. On that occasion Ber and I had foolishly allowed him to host a party in the house.

"Just a few friends now, Stanley," we told him clearly.

"Great!" came the happy reply, "How many does 'a few' mean?"

"No more than ten." I told him firmly. "You can ring your friends up now and invite them over the phone."

Stanley nodded to himself, obviously pleased with the news that his long awaited party was going to become a reality at last. I could see him counting on his fingers as he decided mentally whom to put on his list. I was feeling rather pleased with myself for limiting the number to ten. With Stanley one had to be definite. Ten had to mean ten.

You can imagine our consternation therefore when on the afternoon of his eighth birthday one hundred and twenty-seven children arrived at our house expecting to be fed. Furthermore, Stanley told his guests that it was to be an Animal House party. They all arrived in various animal costumes ranging from pussy cats to wild apes.

It was like feeding time at the zoo as the assorted lions, kangaroos and monkeys fought for their share of the cola,

One hundred and twenty-seven children arrived in various animal cos-tumes ranging from pussy cats to wild apes.

cakes and crisps. There was a traffic jam into the estate from the main road as bewildered parents attempted to deliver their animal costume clad children. The noise was horrendous as Ber and I tried to cater for the hungry hordes and Stanley organised wild safari party games in the garden for his one hundred and twenty-seven friends!

"Sorry Dad!" came the humble apology as we attempted to put the house back together after the party.

"Stanley, you were told to invite ten friends. Your mother counted one hundred and twenty-seven!"

"Sorry! I miscalculated."

"How could you possibly miscalculate by over one hundred?" I asked.

"Well I just kept adding on another one and then another and then I began to lose count! I've only got ten fingers you know!"

The excuse was a lame one. We didn't buy it. Determined that this would never again happen we decided to put a lifetime ban on parties for Stanley. In fact we forbade him to ever use the word "party" again. Thus on the afternoon of his ninth birthday our house was silent and a totally party free zone!

When my parents arrived I was playing football in the garden with Sinéad and Córa. Meanwhile Ber was beating Stanley at chess in the kitchen. This made a pleasant change from simply beating Stanley in the kitchen! Ber never allowed Stanley to win a game of chess. Sometimes she would lead him into thinking that he was going to win and then suddenly call checkmate. This used to frustrate Stanley to the point of explosion. However, he was becoming a better player as a result and was quietly engrossed in his game when Gramps and Nan arrived. The chess was immediately postponed. Everything stopped for Gramps!

Even though Stanley loved his other grandparents he and my father had a very special relationship. A visit from Gramps on his birthday almost at once made up for the absence of a party. Stanley was initially disappointed when he saw no visible evidence of a present on either Gramps or Nan. Maybe they had left it in the car. Maybe it was really small and was lying at the bottom of Nan's handbag or in Gramps' trouser pocket. Maybe however, they didn't buy him anything! Maybe they both felt that he had enough and was getting to be spoilt. All these doubts and maybes however were without foundation. Gramps was full of surprises. He was going to make this a birthday to remember!

Gramps stooped down and stared hard into Stanley's disappointed face.

"How are you today, Stanley?" he asked teasingly.

"I'm fine, Gramps!" Stanley replied politely. "It's my birthday today!" he added just in case they had forgotten.

"Your birthday! My goodness! We better do something about that right away!"

A broad smile appeared on Stanley's face.

"Come along Stanley! Your carriage awaits!" command-ed Gramps in a deep, posh, theatrical voice which usually meant something exciting was about to happen.

"Carriage?" asked Stanley who although confused was enjoying his grandfather's playful mystery.

"Well actually it's a 1967 Volkswagen Beetle. But it's got loads of horse power. Now come along." And he headed out through the front door with Stanley in hot pursuit. "But where are we going, Gramps?" asked Stanley delightedly. He was already in the back seat as his grandfather started up the engine.

"A magical mystery tour, my boy! A magical mystery tour!" Then he sang out full belt that wonderful Beatles song of the same name. "The magical mystery tour is com-ing to take you away .. Coming to take you away...take you away!"

Stanley joined in the singing and the duo sounded like a pair of screeching cats!

I tapped on the driver's window as the car began to move slowly on the gravel driveway.

"Can I come too?" I asked, hoping to be included in the adventure.

"Only if you promise to join in the singing!" ordered Gramps.

"Of course!" I replied.

"And only if you promise to buy me a pint on the way home and Stanley as much coke as his belly can hold!"

"Done!" I agreed and I was sitting in the passenger seat raring to go.

We set off at great speed as the ancient car tore along the road noisily. The engine chugged and roared sending vibrations up through the seats, tickling our behinds and making us shudder. It was so noisy in the car that it was difficult to hear one another speaking. Conversations were thus ended. Each of us sat alone with his thoughts, brimming over with both happiness and excitement. There we were, three generations of McGregor, but at that moment there was no age difference. We were all equally boylike enjoying our adventure.

Gramps drove like a lunatic! This was nothing new. He always drove like one. On this occasion he certainly showed no signs of improving his driving skills. He changed gears abruptly and braked without warning, throwing his passengers forward each time. He also drove far too quickly, causing near heart failure in both those inside the vehicle and those outside it, particularly oncoming motorists.

He had chosen the coastal road for our mystery route on which he drove at breakneck speed. This road, although visually stunning with some breathtaking views of the bay, is also pretty treacherous. It winds its way around three mountains and at the higher points it narrows to an almost single lane. At stretches it is unwise to look out the window as there are many cliff faces which fall to the ocean several hundred feet below. Stanley and I clung to our seats as

Gramps sped along, zipping around each hairpin bend apparently unaware of any danger!

Gramps sang the whole way keeping rhythm on the steering wheel which he used as a finger drum.

"She loves you yeah yeah yeah!
She loves you yeah yeah yeah!
And with a love like that!
You know you should be glad! Yeah yeah yeah!"

His froglike voice croaked out Beatles songs and operatic arias one after the other. With a voice like his it was difficult to tell the difference.

At last we came to a halt. It was, needless to say, an abrupt one. We were thrown forward in our seats as Gramps braked too suddenly then jerked the handbrake upright. For good measure we were thrown forward a second time as he left the car in gear before turning off the engine.

"Just testing," he said as he corrected his mistake. It was one of those times when I wasn't sure whether he was being serious or simply joking!

Stanley and I got out of the car and followed Gramps as he led us on the second leg of this magical mystery tour.

"Stage two, gentlemen!" he announced in his theatrical voice again, "will take the form of a short trek. Please follow."

He had parked the car at the foot of the third mountain and we had now left the road and were making our way across some very stony fields. At the far end of these fields we climbed over some steep rocks, a few of which were slippery underfoot. With each of us over the final obstacles safely we finally reached our destination.

We found ourselves in a small sheltered bay. There was a beach of wonderfully golden sand which rose to form miniature mountainlike dunes. Running in a perfectly straight line out into the sea was a short narrow pier. Some fishing boats were moored here and they bobbed up and down almost merrily, in rhythm with the gentle tide. With the sun scorching down from a clear blue sea, it was indeed a most beautiful sight to behold. Oddly though for such a fine summer's day, we were the only people on the beach.

"This is a smashing place, Gramps!" exclaimed Stanley, as his eyes darted back and forth from the sand dunes to the sea.

"It sure is Dad," I agreed, "How come you never brought us here before?"

"It's a private beach. It belongs to Dan Fogarty. He's going to build some holiday chalets in those fields where we were walking and develop it as a sea angling holiday centre," Gramps explained matter of factly.

Dan Fogarty was both my father's boss and friend for many years. My parents managed one of Dan's hotels before they both retired.

"Come on men!" ordered Gramps again "Stage three!"

"But Gramps, we can't go swimming. We didn't bring

our swimming gear. We don't have any towels or anything." complained Stanley.

"I didn't bring you here to swim," said Gramps.

"You didn't?" Stanley was now really confused.

Still enjoying the mystery, we once again followed Gramps who trudged through the sand towards the pier. As we walked along the pier Gramps suddenly grabbed Stanley and lifted him over his shoulder in "fireman's lift" style.

"Will I throw you in?" he joked as he playfully neared the edge of the pier with Stanley wriggling and screeching wildly.

Remembering all the crazy things Stanley had done in the past I roared my approval.

"Go ahead Dad! Throw him in head first! Only tie a brick around his ankles first!"

Without warning and with Stanley still perched high over his head, Gramps stepped off the edge of the pier. Both he and Stanley fell about three feet where they landed on the deck of a fishing boat. As they clambered to their feet Gramps beckoned me to come and join them on board!

"Now, Stanley," he began as he dusted himself down, "read what it says on the side of this boat."

Stanley, although still bewildered after his tumble, was utterly engrossed in the adventure. He peered over the side of the boat and read out loud.

It says...." he paused in disbelief, "It says, 'STANLEY AND GRAMPS'!"

He was dumbfounded. So was I!

"It is both your boat and mine, Stanley! I bought it out of my retirement money. Dan has given me the okay to moor it here all year round," explained Gramps excitedly. It was a beautiful white power boat with a green stripe on both sides. On the front was a covered-in area where the engine and controls were kept. At the opposite end was a small enclosed cabin area.

"I think it's time to give the birthday boy his present now!" announced Gramps. "Go into the cabin, Stanley and open it!" Stanley entered the cabin, which was a tiny transparent structure with a wooden bench, a small table, a primus stove and some storage cupboards. On the bench was placed a long gift-wrapped present. Stanley tore off the paper and screeched with delight.

"A fishing rod!"

"Correct!" said Gramps rather obviously, "Now it's time for me to open mine!" He then pulled out another gift-wrapped parcel.

He read the card out loud before opening it.

"'To Gramps, Love Always, Gramps'!"

We all laughed heartily as he tore off the paper in the same excited manner as his grandson. It was of course an identical fishing rod to that of Stanley's.

"Together we will catch every fish in the sea!" he roared and the two of them danced up and down on the deck of the boat. They waved their rods in the air like two swords. As Gramps and Stanley prepared to rid the oceans of the world of their fish population, one point suddenly occurred to me. My father had never fished in his life. Neither to my knowledge had he ever driven a power boat.

"Dad?" I asked when the dancing had stopped, "Do you know anything about fishing?"

"Not a thing!" he replied happily, "But I'm going to learn with Stanley. Dan is going to show me how to steer this ocean liner here and he's promised to give us a few lessons! No problem, eh Stanley?"

"No problem, Gramps!" roared Stanley delightedly.

"Now let the party begin!" ordered Gramps.

Gramps moved into the tiny cabin where he boiled a kettle on the primus stove. He opened a cupboard and produced a packet of digestives and a swiss roll. He stuck nine candles into the swiss roll and lit them. Stanley was laughing so much he couldn't blow out the candles. As we ate our cake and drank tea from enamel mugs Gramps entertained us with all his old jokes. We had heard them all before but we laughed anyway.

"What's green, hairy and travels at sixty miles an hour backwards?"

"Tell us, Gramps."

"A homesick gooseberry!"

"How did the punk rocker cross the road?"

"How, Gramps?"

"He was stapled to the chicken!"

On the way home we stopped at a pub where as promised I bought Gramps his pint of Guinness and Stanley a bottle of coke. We sat there for over an hour listening to more jokes and Gramps singing all his favourite songs. The barman gave him a funny look every now and again but neither Stanley nor Gramps seemed to notice. When it was time to go I insisted on driving. It was bad enough being a passenger of Gramps when he hadn't had a pint of Guinness!

The journey home was slow and silent. Stanley drifted off to sleep on the back seat, while Gramps snored gently next to me in the front. They had both laughed and sung themselves into a state of exhaustion. The following day at breakfast Stanley announced that it had been the best birthday anybody had ever had anywhere at any time. Thanks to Gramps!

Stanley and Gramps soon became quite expert at both sea angling and boating. Once he had developed enough

Stanley and I listened to all of Gramps' jokes.

confidence with both the rod and the boat Gramps decided to take charge. From then on it became a Stanley and Gramps partnership only. Grandfather and grandson would leave early every Sunday morning and return to dry land after dark. They would bring a big basket of food and bottles of lemonade to sustain them during their long hours at sea. Apart from fishing, the day was spent chatting about each other's lives.

When he was with his grandfather Stanley was a different human being. Gone was the madness which he continued to display at home and at school. In some extraordinary way my father was able to relate to Stanley like nobody else in his life. My mother always maintained that Gramps found it easy to relate to children because he himself had never grown up! He was always saying funny things to Stanley. He phoned Stanley up one evening. "What's the matter, Gramps?" asked Stanley. "Your grandmother sent me to bed early!" came the tearful reply.

"Why?" laughed Stanley.

"Just because I dunked my big toe into my boiled egg!"

Another time he came into our kitchen wearing a gold fish bowl on his head!

"When I grow up, Stanley, I want to be an astronaut!"

"But Gramps! Nan told me that you were sixty-nine years old!"

"Damn it Stanley! I'm too young! I'll have to wait until I'm a big boy!"

Stanley loved this playfulness and thus his Sunday fishing trip became the high point of the week. Gramps was a wonderful storyteller and could compose the most imaginative tales of horror and suspense with bloodthirsty details and thrilling climaxes. However, nothing pleased Stanley more than listening to Gramps recalling his own life.

He loved to hear how as a young man his grandfather played for West Bromwich Albion until a badly damaged knee ended his promising sporting career. After a long list of various jobs ranging from cinema usher to security officer he eventually returned to Ireland where both he and my mother managed Dan Fogarty's hotel. From these stories Stanley learned so much about his family he quickly became an expert, recalling dates and events instantly.

He was able to tell me the exact date I started school, the name of my first teacher and even what I had for my lunch. He had all the details of my first football match including the embarrassing fact that I had scored an own goal! Most of his sentences began with, "Gramps told me..." or "Gramps said that..."! Still, despite my son discovering secrets of my childhood, I was delighted that he was so close to his grandfather. I welcomed the arrival of each Sunday when I was sure of a peaceful Stanley free day. However, like all good things, that too was to come to an end!

Chapter 9
Moving On

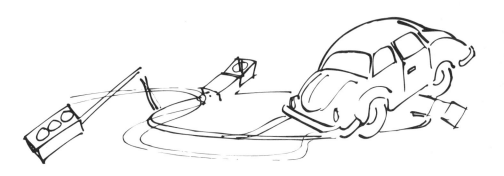

When Gramps lost his driving licence it seemed for a while that the fishing trips would have to come to an end. Gramps was furious at the judge's decision.

"Banned from driving for twelve months! Just because I didn't see that red light! What is the world coming too when a man isn't allowed to make a simple driving error?" he complained as we drove him home from the court after the hearing. Stanley decided to give his grandfather some moral support.

"It's ridiculous, Gramps! All you did was knock over a couple of those silly bollards. Stupid place to put them anyway. Out in the middle of the road! They were bound to get knocked down sooner or later!"

However, I for one agreed with the judge. Gramps not only went through a red light at a busy intersection, but he also sped down a one way street before turning wildly and crashing into a set of bollards in the middle of a pedestrian crossing. The hearing lasted a mere five minutes. Gramps was advised to plead guilty to the five charges for which he received his twelve month ban and a fifty pounds fine.

"And I hope sir, that after the twelve months expire that you continue to occupy a passenger seat. Our roads might then be a little safer," came the stern words from the judge.

As we neared his grandparents' house Stanley suddenly was struck by a disturbing thought.

"Gramps! That means we won't be able to go fishing any more!"

"I know Stan. And I have just finished a book on shark fishing!" There followed a long dull silence until Stanley cheerfully announced,

"I've just had a brilliant idea!"

I hated these *brilliant ideas*. They usually involved trouble or else me or sometimes even both. This time it was both!

"Dad can drive us! He can even come along and join in the fishing!" It was one of those "you're-not-going-to-get-out-of-this-one-situations". I tried pathetically.

"You don't want me around. I'll only be in the way!"

"Nonsense! Stanley and I will have you hauling in whoppers in no time!" beamed Gramps who knew I wasn't enthusiastic but wasn't taking "no" for an answer.

"You can pick me up on Sunday at seven thirty and we'll be out on the waves by nine!" he ordered as he pulled himself out of the car, a little less worried about his earlier punishment.

"Dad!" came Stanley's voice from the back seat as we made our way to our own house.

"Yes, Stanley?"

"You're a sound man!"

He was lucky there were no bollards in the middle of the road as on hearing that I would surely have driven straight into them. The prospect of losing my one day of guaranteed peace almost sent me into a deep depression. To make matters worse I would now be spending my time alone in a boat with Stanley and his grandfather instead of being in a house where there was no Stanley to cause me the slightest grief for at least ten hours. However, I realised that for the next twelve months at least, I had no choice.

From that following Sunday on I became part of the "McGregor-Three-Generation-Fishing-Crew". Despite my initial reluctance I soon got into the swing of things. Stanley insisted on teaching me.

"This way Dad," he would say as he held the rod the right way round for me. "Now give it a good jerk! That's the way! Good man! He's learning Gramps!"

"Ah sure he's not a bad lad at all! And he was always a bit of a jerk!" would come Gramps' cynical reply.

Stanley was right, I did learn and soon I became as

enthusiastic as them both. Each trip was hugely enjoyable and we always managed to catch something which we invariably cooked for supper. Very often we returned with far too many fish. Stanley would then knock on every door on the estate offering free samples of the day's catch. Stanley felt that we should have charged for the fish until I reminded him of the importance of being neighbourly. The neighbours however were not to enjoy Stanley's free fresh fish for long.

*   *   *   *   *   *   *   *   *

During that summer we had a weekend visit from my cousin Paul, the farmer from Kilkenny who many years previously had adopted Zapper. He and his wife Ann invited Stanley to return to their farm to spend a few days with them.

"He won't go, Paul!" I said on hearing the invitation. "Stanley's a home bird. Aren't you, Stan?"

But Stanley didn't hear me. He was upstairs already packing his bags. Within minutes he was back again with his luggage in both hands.

"Okay Paul! Let's go!"

He couldn't wait! The prospect of spending time on a farm fascinated Stanley. He was also looking forward to being reunited with his old, and by now *very* old, friend Zapper.

Although the invitation was initially for a few days Stanley stayed for seven weeks and would have stayed forever had the opportunity been offered. At the outset both Ber and I were worried in case Stanley might suffer from homesickness. He had never been away from home for any long period of time apart from a weekend in Kerry with the cubs. That wasn't even a full weekend. We were asked to come and collect him on the Saturday morning after he accidently set fire to the main tent while attempting to put out the camp fire. He was asked to leave the cubs after that!

We were also afraid that Stanley would miss his twin sisters. He loved Córa and Sinéad and played the role of big brother to a tee. He brought them to the pictures, to the library, and to the shops. He even taught them how to play pool in the local snooker hall! As Paul and Ann had no children, we felt that after a few days Stanley would miss his sisters so much he would demand to be brought home. How mistaken we were!

After only two days on the farm, Stanley believed that an agricultural life was the only life for him. He strolled through the green fields of Paul's farm with Zapper lagging tiredly behind him. He felt like the Lord of the Manor. It didn't matter to him that there were no children with whom he could play. Surrounded by fields, tractors, trailers, dung spreaders and in the company of farm animals he felt completely at home. He phoned on the second night of his stay.

"Dad don't worry about me! I'm a farmer now! I never want to come home!"

Before I had a chance to say or ask anything he hung up! He didn't phone again that week but we did receive a letter at the beginning of the second week. It read:

Dear Dad, Mum, Sinéad and Córa,

This is the most brilliant, the most fantastic, the most fabulous, bestest, maddest, coolest place in the whole wide world! Thanks for letting me stay here Mum and Dad. I really love it. Paul and Ann really love having me here too.

Even though Paul doesn't say a lot I think he really appreciates all I do for him around the place. I help him with everything and I'm becoming an expert. Yesterday evening after milking he looked at me and said, "Stanley, you're something else!" Even though I'm not quite sure what he meant I'm pretty certain that he likes me a lot. It's great for you to know that I'm very popular here isn't it!

Oh I nearly forgot to tell you. I can drive a tractor now. I taught myself how. I figured there wasn't much point in becoming a farmer if I couldn't drive a tractor. Paul got a little annoyed with me when I first started to learn which I think was a little unfair. I didn't see his new Volvo

parked in the farmyard. I haven't got eyes in the
back of my head. If you ask me it's a dopey place
to park a new car, especially with so much farm
machinery around the place. Anything might happen.

I think Paul over-reacted. He started yelling
and screaming at me and using some very rude
words. I told him that the last time I used those

words I had to wash my mouth out with soap and was grounded for a week. I didn't understand what all the fuss was about. The crane was eventually able to lift the tractor off the bonnet. All that shouting and roaring just because the Volvo needed a couple of new doors and a few bits and pieces for the engine. I told him to calm down and not to worry about the repair costs, that you were really rich and there would be no problem.

Anyway, I'm now absolutely brilliant at driving the tractor, now that I've discovered the difference between forward and reverse. It's also been a great help since I found the brake. I go for a practice every morning before Paul calls me for breakfast. He has a very unusual way of telling me that breakfast is ready. He chases me as I zoom around the field, waving his arms and screaming. He really is such a funny guy! I can never hear what he is saying though as it's really noisy in the tractor cab. Even noisier than Gramps' Beetle.

Zapper sends her love. She still loves me a lot. Even though she hadn't seen me since I was three she recognised me immediately. She got really excited and started running madly through the fields. Paul said he hadn't seen her run like that for years. She's about twelve now which in doggy years makes her about ninety. Still, since I came she bounces around the place like a puppy. She's so thrilled to see me again after all these years she actually cries when I go to pat her.

All the other animals are great too. I feel sorry for them though, especially the cows. They just munch grass all day in the same fields. They must get really bored. I decided to take them for a little walk the other day. Myself and the cows headed to the park.

I was hoping that they would have a great time but they don't know how to enjoy themselves. They wouldn't go near the sandpit or the paddling pool. All they wanted to do was to munch some silly looking flowers in these flower beds. The park attendant was really angry. Grumpy old sod! He came over shaking his fist at me.

"Get those bloody cows out of there!" he roared. There were spits flying out of his mouth he was so mad.

"Don't worry buster!" I told him, "And we won't be coming back either. There's nothing for these poor cows to do only eat your flowers. They could do that at home if they wanted!"

The cows really like me now. I think they appreciate how nice I was to take them for a walk. Every time they see me they start mooing extra loudly and hopping up and down. The other evening at milking they were so happy to see me coming into the parlour that they ran to the entrance to greet me. I had to stand out of their way before they stampeded me into the ground. Still I suppose it's their way of showing their affection.

I've got to go now folks because I think I can hear Paul going out. He's taking some pigs to the mart so I said I'd give him a hand. I'm brilliant with pigs too.

This place is great. It's great for Paul and Ann to have such a helpful guy like me around isn't it?

I miss you both a little bit and Córa and Sinéad a lot. Tell them I'll bring them back something nice. Maybe a pet pig or a sheep. Paul has loads of them so I'm sure he won't miss one or two.

See you soon,

Stanley.

Having read the letter my hands were shaking. Poor Paul and Ann! They don't have children, how in the name of goodness were they going to put up with Stanley? There was however, a second letter that morning. It was from Paul. It read:

Dear Pat and Ber,

You both have often told me just how crazy your son is. I have heard many tales of his exploits, which, I must admit, I felt had to be exaggerated. However, having spent more than a week in his company, I regret to have to tell you this. Your son is a human time bomb.

He seems to think there is nothing wrong with driving my tractor. I have begged him not to drive it but every time I do so he seems to think I'm joking. The more I beg and plead the funnier he thinks I am. The first day he was here he tried to start up the tractor. Instead he threw it into reverse and came crashing into the farmyard. Because he couldn't find the brake, he ended up colliding into my brand new Volvo. The tractor crushed the car up against the wall of the barn where its front wheel became imbedded in the bonnet. I had to hire a crane to have the tractor extricated from the Volvo. Thankfully there was nobody in the farmyard at the time. I'm not complaining about the costs as Ann's brother owns a garage and actually owes me a few favours so he has agreed to cover the repairs. By the way Pat, Stanley tells me that you are now a millionaire. Funny how you never mentioned that before!

Stanley also seems to think that all animals are pets and regularly takes them out. He has taken the cows to the park and plans to take the pigs shopping with him! Zapper is terrified of him. She fled the moment she saw him and if he stays much longer the poor old girl will die of fright. The cows aren't too pleased when he's around either. The other evening at milking they stampeded out of the parlour when he arrived to give a hand. It took me ages to get them back in again.

Speaking of milking, Stanley made rather a mess of things the first evening he was here. He climbed on top of a vat to see the milk as it cooled. However, he lost his balance and fell in complete with manure-covered boots and mud-stained clothes. I had to dump that evening's milk.

The most worrying aspect of his stay however is that he loves it here. He plans to move here permanently when he leaves school and become a full time farmhand. Please Pat, talk him out of it! He's a nice kid but to be brutally honest if I thought he was ever going to come back on a permanent basis I would sell up and emigrate! I've told Stanley he can stay for another week or two if he likes. I've also told him he can go home any time he feels like it. I hope he feels like it soon!

Where in the name of God did you get him? Your bewildered cousin,

Paul.

My immediate reaction to reading the letter would have been to hop into the car, drive to Kilkenny and bring Stanley home. However, Ber refused to react in this way.

"Calm down!" she advised, "Obviously things haven't got any worse otherwise Paul would have driven him back himself by now."

I took her advice. After a couple of days had passed I telephoned Paul. He laughed when I asked him how Stanley was getting on. He was still driving them crazy but the situation was no worse. I asked him to ring me in the event of a major emergency. Thankfully there was no such phone call.

After seven weeks Stanley returned home full of stories about his exciting farm adventures. However he wasn't the only one with exciting news to tell.

While Stanley was in Kilkenny I received a letter from Toledo University, Ohio, U.S.A. I had applied for a position of visiting lecturer for one year. To my amazement I was accepted. I was delighted to be offered such an opportunity. Ber was as excited as I was at the prospect of us all going to the U.S.A. She told me to ring immediately and accept the offer. Gramps too was full of encouragement.

"Go for it son! We'll be over to visit at Christmas!" he beamed.

Stanley danced around the house singing "Here we go! Here we go! Here we go!" when we told him. He immediately lost himself in an huge atlas as he searched for Toledo, Ohio.

"Here it is Dad!" he roared when he found it. "South west of Lake Erie! We can do some great fishing there! Not too far from Detroit or Cleveland either!"

Suddenly the boy who had recently made up his mind to become a farmer had changed it again.

"You never know, Dad," he said as his imagination rolled around and around, "We might stay there longer than a year! We might stay there forever! One day I might even become Stanley Paul Francis McGregor, President of the United States of America!" A smile broadened across his impish eleven year old face. "Look out America!" he screamed with joy, "Here I come!"

Watch out for another great book from

BLACKWATER PRESS

"Return to Troy"
by
Pierce C. Feirtear

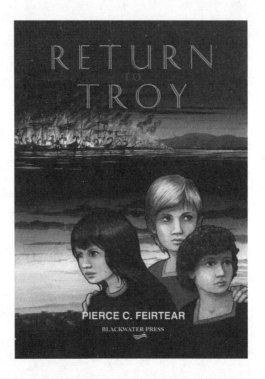

The war in Troy has been raging for ten long years. Areon, Nesa and
Osban cannot remember the world outside the Great Wall. When an
opportunity arises to re-discover this world they decide to take it.
It is a decision they will regret for a long time…